The Big Lakes of Lakeland

Alan Smith

RIGG SIDE PUBLICATIONS

INTRODUCTION

The Lake District is a special place and it is the big lakes in particular that make it special. This may be a self evident truth, but the point is worth making. Not only does the Lake District National Park contain the four largest lakes of England and Wales, but also the deepest and without doubt the most picturesque set of lakes of any small upland area of these islands. Most of the upland National Parks of England and Wales bear the name either of the highest mountain (Snowdonia), or the most prominent peaks or upland areas (Brecon Beacons or Dartmoor), but the Lake District National Park is different. In spite of having England's highest peak in Scafell Pike it is the lakes that personify its character and label the area in people's minds.

There are well over a thousand sheets of fresh water in Lakeland – from minute ponds, peaty pools, reservoirs, upland and lowland tarns up to lakes the size of Windermere, England's largest lake at over 17 kms. long. This book concentrates on the seventeen big lakes of the National Park. Most people cannot fail to see at least one of these if they come here. These big lakes give their names to the regional areas of the Park. They are the ones where people flock to their shores, where they sail, row, swim, sit beside or walk alongside. They have been photographed, painted, written about, eulogised in poetry and in every way epitomise this extraordinary piece of upland Britain.

This book will focus on the lakes as part of the landscape. It will describe the features of the lakes and explain why they are as they are. It will explore their origins, how they were shaped, how they change and evolve and what perhaps is their ultimate fate. It will explain the striking differences between the big lakes – the rockiness of some, the lowland mellow character of others. It is the shoreline features that most people experience – the bays, islands, peninsulas and beaches. The emphasis in this book is on what the visitor can see and easily understand. It will not cover all the details that are known about life in the lakes, the flora and fauna or the complexities of the freshwater ecology. It does not tackle the problems of pollution or become involved with the issues of recreational pressure and use. It is hoped that this will be seen as an easy to read account of the landscape features of the lakes, a little about their history and origins and as a starter to learning more about this extraordinary piece of the English landscape.

It is intended that the smaller lakes and tarns of Lakeland will be covered in the next volume (No.6) of this *Landscapes of Cumbria Series*.

3

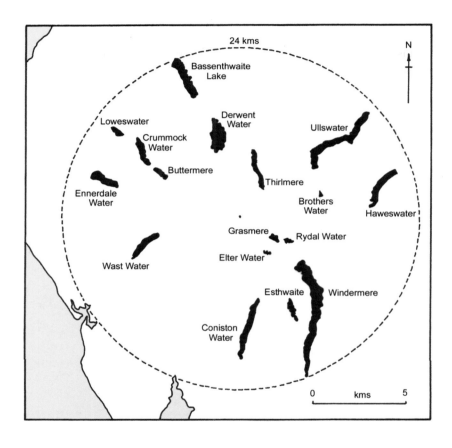

Figure 1. The Seventeen Big Lakes.
The circle is of a 24 km (15 mile) radius centred on an imaginary point
in the heart of the Lakeland fells

A PATTERN OF LAKES

The poet William Wordsworth in his *'Guide to the Lakes'* published initially in 1810, was one of the first writers to draw attention to the radial nature of the Lake District drainage pattern, the major valleys diverging ...."like spokes from the nave of a wheel ". All of the 17 big lakes described in this book lie in the floors of these major radiating valleys. In fact it will be seen that it is the lake basins themselves, more than the stream lines as such, that display this strong radial arrangement. It is actually possible to come up with an imaginary point in the heart of the district and draw a neat circle of approximately 24 km (15 mile) radius and enclose all the major lake basins (Figure 1). This piece of visual trickery really emphasises the wheel-like configuration of the topography.

The 17 big lakes vary enormously in both size and character – see table overleaf. Windermere is far and away the largest and longest. Not only is it nearly twice the size of Ullswater, the second in the list, but it is also England's largest lake. By comparison it is nearly 75 times larger than Elter Water, the smallest of the 'big lakes'. The floors of three of the lakes – Windermere, Coniston Water and Wast Water lie below sea level, pointing to the magnitude of the erosive forces that must have excavated these basins. Several of the lakes have more than one deep basin, noticeably Windermere which has distinct northern and southern basins, separated by a shallow area in its middle near Belle Isle. Ullswater has three distinct basins in its floor. Bassenthwaite Lake and Ennerdale Water, although large lakes, have extensive shallow water areas. Some of the smaller lakes, Elter Water and Esthwaite for example, were clearly larger stretches of water in the past, indicating that processes of infilling are going on and need to be explained.

Two lakes, Thirlmere and Haweswater have been radically altered by damming to provide large water supply reservoirs, consequently both of these are now far deeper, wider and longer than the original natural lakes.

All of these big lakes are what geologists call 'piedmont lakes' – but the older, less precise term 'ribbon lakes' is a far better description of their shape and pattern. Virtually all the lakes lie as long, narrow ribbons of water along the valley floors, many times longer than they are wide. Only Derwent Water really stands out as a relatively broad lake, but the reasons for that can be explained.

The pattern of lakes raises another interesting question. Lakes exist in virtually all of the radiating major valleys, but why not in Eskdale, Dunnerdale, Great Langdale and Longsleddale – all deep valley troughs and major spokes in Wordsworth's wheel ? We must ponder that in later sections.

The 17 big lakes in order of size (surface area)

	Surface area kms²	Height above OD m.	Maximum Depth m.
1. Windermere	14.76	39.3	64
2. Ullswater	8.94	145.0	62.5
3. Derwent Water	5.35	74.5	22
4. Bassenthwaite Lake	5.28	68.8	19
5. Coniston Water	4.91	43.5	56.1
6. Haweswater (present lake) (original lake)	3.90 1.38	239.8 210.9	57 28
7. Thirlmere (present lake) (original lake)	3.26 1.34	179.1 162.5	46 29.4
8. Ennerdale Water	2.99	112.3	42
9. Wast Water	2.91	61.0	76
10. Crummock Water	2.52	98.0	43.9
11. Esthwaite Water	1.00	65.4	15.5
12. Buttermere	0.94	101.0	28.6
13. Grasmere	0.64	61.7	21.5
14 Loweswater	0.64	121.4	16
15. Rydal Water	0.33	53.0	19
16. Brothers Water	0.21	158.0	16.7
17. Elter Water	0.19	55.0	7.5

The spellings of the lake names used in the table above, are as shown on current Ordnance Survey 1:25,000 Explorer maps. These spellings are used throughout the book. Slightly different spellings will be found in use in other publications and on signage.

SOUNDING THE LAKES

Cumbria was one of the last counties in Britain to be surveyed by the Ordnance Survey. It was late in the 1860's when the first large scale (six inches to the mile) maps became available, providing for the first time accurate representations of the outlines and shoreline details of the big lakes. The work of the Ordnance Survey did not however, extend to measuring the depths of the lakes and producing bathymetric contouring. This had to wait many years before a variety of individuals and private organisations came forward to sound the lake basins and provide details of their shapes and depths. It is interesting that even today the current Ordnance Survey 1:25,000 Explorer maps, such splendid detailed maps of the Lakeland terrain, simply show the lakes in blue shading with no information on their depth and no bathymetric contouring. The smaller scale 1:50,000 Landranger maps do show contour values at 10m intervals for the largest lakes.

There are several early records of soundings of the lakes, most notably those of Peter Crosthwaite of Keswick between 1783 and 1794. His work was published in 1809 as a set of maps of eight of the main lakes, with scattered depth measurements and a great deal of shoreline detail. Around the same time a local land surveyor James Clark published a similar work in 1787 on *'A Survey of the Lakes of Cumberland, Westmorland and Lancashire'*. The first systematic measurement of most of the lake basins had to wait until 1895 when Dr Hugh Robert Mill published his results of his detailed *'Bathymetrical Survey of the English Lakes'*. This was an extensive piece of work, including not only maps and details of the sounding of ten of the major lakes but the first commentary on the configuration of the lakes in the district, along with some basic limnology and a description of the features of the lake basins. Mill's work was a classic piece of individual late Victorian scientific enquiry. His description of the methods used paints a picture of a rather gentile summer spent in the Lake District, probably in 1893, using simple surveying equipment and making systematic and accurate measurements which were checked and rechecked with great diligence. He worked from a rowing boat sounding the depths of the water using "a well-twisted hemp line about three-quarters of an inch in circumference ... that had been soaked, stretched and dried repeatedly ... and marked with tufts of coloured worsted twisted through the strands at every fathom". A 5lb lead weight was attached to the bottom of the rope. A brass tube was also attached so as to bring up a sample of the bottom mud where possible. Occasional observations of water temperature were also taken. A series of straight line traverses were made across the lakes taking soundings at regular intervals. A sextant was used for position finding and an

Abney Level for measuring lake surface levels against convenient Ordnance Survey bench marks. He did not employ local boatmen ...."their rowing was often found to vary in strength and they showed a strong aversion to continue working in rain". On most of the lakes his friend, Mr Heawood rowed, while he himself took the soundings. Mrs Mill (with hat in Figure 2), steered and kept the notebooks. A number of other individuals are named as helpers. The Ordnance Survey was involved and supportive, and it is noted that Mr Heawood drew the maps (by hand) and did the calculations on depth and volume in the Ordnance Survey offices in Southampton. The expenses for the whole project were defrayed by the Royal Geographical Society, who published the material in 1895. Mill's work remains to this day a valuable source of data on the lake basins.

Figure 2.
Mill sounding the lakes, with Heawood rowing and Mrs Mill (in hat) steering and keeping the notebooks.

Since Mill's work a number of other agencies and organisations have taken on the work of sounding the lake basins. Notably absent from Mill's survey was Thirlmere, which at the time was under consideration by Manchester Corporation for conversion to a water supply reservoir. In 1937 the Freshwater Biological Association, based by Windermere, carried out echo-sounding measurements on Windermere and produced a more accurate chart of our largest lake. After that project, the equipment was retained and FBA staff completed further surveys, notably of some of the smaller lakes. In the period after World War II the Brathay Exploration Group, along with college and university groups, continued the work on the smaller lakes and tarns of the Lake District, notably in the context of the present book on Rydal Water, Brothers Water and Elter Water.

MAP V.   THE GEOGRAPHICAL JOURNAL 1895

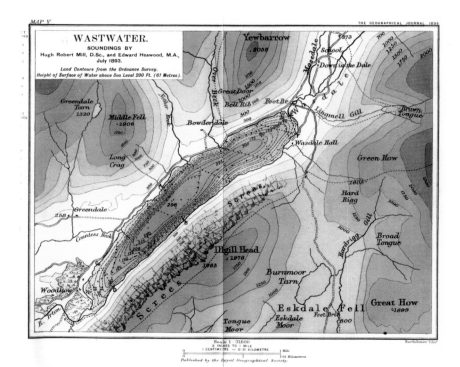

Figure 3.

An example of Mill's work, in this case the map for Wast Water.

Each map in his booklet showed the bathymetric contours and lines of traverse. The surrounding topography was shown layer coloured.

Accompanying each map were representative long and cross sections of the lake.

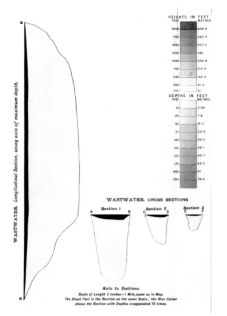

THE LAKES AND GEOLOGY

The Lakeland landscape is shaped by its geology. Different rock types stamp their own characteristics on the detailed shapes of the fells and dales. The boundary of the district we recognise as the Lake District is largely defined by its geology. Old, resistant rocks make up the mountainous core. Younger, weaker rocks underlie the surrounding lowlands. (Figure 4).

There is little evidence however, that the position and radial configuration of the 17 big lakes across the district has been significantly determined by local variation of rock type. All the big lakes lie well within the central mountain core, and thus in a general way relate to geology. They are however, particularly confined to the floors of the major glaciated troughs which cut deep into the heart of the fells. None of the lakes extend out on to the weaker rocks of the lowlands. Their positions emphasise the radial nature of the drainage pattern of the district and demonstrate the outward movement of the glaciers from a central ice dome. Most of the main valleys cut across the underlying geological structures and outcrops. Whether the radial pattern of the drainage is an old inherited feature or whether it is a direct result of the radial movement of the ice is a matter of debate. Glaciers were equally effective in carving out lake basins into all the major rock types that make up the mountainous core of the district.

Of the seventeen big lakes, four (Bassenthwaite Lake, Derwent Water, Crummock Water and Lowes Water) lie entirely on rocks of the Skiddaw Group. These are complex mudstones, siltstones, slates and sand-stones, heavily folded and cleaved and much altered by metamorphism from their original state of deep water marine sediments. Five of the lakes (Thirlmere, Grasmere, Rydal Water, Brothers Water and Elter Water) lie on the Borrowdale Volcanic Group rocks that form the core area of central Lakeland. These are a resistant mixture of lavas, volcanic ashes and reworked volcanic debris. Coniston Water and Esthwaite in south Lakeland lie on the hard Silurian sedimentary rocks (sandstones, grits and shales) of the Windermere Supergroup. Windermere itself also largely falls into this latter category, only its extreme northern tip extending a very short way on to the volcanic rocks.

The other five lakes extend across a variety of rock types. Ullswater is predominantly on the volcanics, but the complex geological structures of its lower reaches brings Skiddaw Group rocks and Devonian age conglomerates to its shores. Haweswater, Ennerdale Water and Wast Water are dominated by volcanic rocks but all also cross granitic and other intrusive igneous rocks.

Buttermere similarly has volcanic, intrusive igneous rocks and Skiddaw Group materials along its shores.

Looked at more locally, geology is of great significance in explaining the detailed topography of the big lakes. The actual shape of some of the lakes owes much to the variation in rock type. A striking example is the 'dog-legged' shape of Ullswater with its three distinct reaches which relates to the structures and outcrop patterns of the underlying rocks. In many lakes harder rocks stand out as peninsulas and promontories, whereas bays are cut back on weaker strata. Beach material along the lake shores varies with rock type. Islands often relate to local geology. The calibre and amount of rock debris brought down from the fells and deposited into the lake basins by streams also varies greatly on different geological terrains.

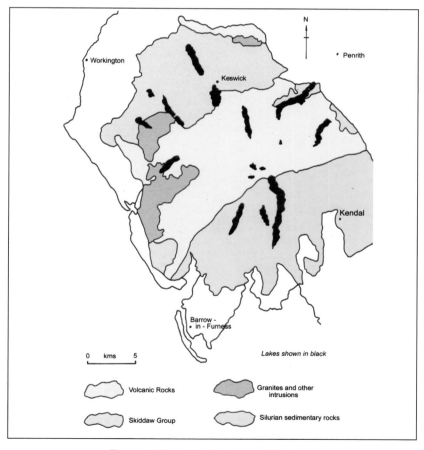

Figure 4. The lake basins and Geology

11

HOW WERE THE LAKES FORMED?

"….The long lakes dammed in the scoop of the dales"

Norman Nicholson
The Bow in the Cloud IV
Five Rivers 1944

The Cumbrian poet Norman Nicholson nicely encapsulates the answer to this question in this evocative line from one of his earliest poems. In essence there are two ways to create a stretch of water like a lake in the landscape – 'scoop out a hole' or 'create a dam', or do both. The natural processes of landscape development over the last tens of thousands of years in Lakeland have seen both employed.

All the big lakes of Lakeland were created by the work of ice during the last ice age. Powerful glaciers scooped out deep basins in the rocky floors of the main valleys and in a few cases also left behind piles of glacial debris which helped further in damming up water and retaining the lakes. The process of ice excavating the rocky valley floors was, however, far and away the most significant.

EXCAVATING ROCK BASINS

The story of the Ice Age in the Lake District was the topic of *No. 3* in this series of booklets on *'The Landscapes of Cumbria'*. The major lake basins were all created by ice during the **Last Glacial Maximum** of the recent ice ages – a stage which peaked around 21,000 years ago. During that time a great ice sheet, a dome of ice, lay over the Lakeland fells, completely covering the landscape with perhaps only the highest western fell tops of the Scafell range, Bowfell, Great Gable and Pillar protruding. Ice had been building up for thousands of years. It was flowing over the landscape and streaming down the main valleys, outwards in all directions from the core of the central Lakeland fells to the lower ground of the Eden Valley, the Solway Plain, the Irish Sea Basin and Morecambe Bay (Figure 5). By about 13,550 years ago the ice sheet had waned, the valley glaciers had melted away and a new landscape of ice scoured fells and lakes left impounded in the valley floors was revealed.

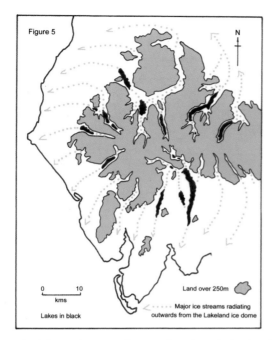

Figure 5

0   10
kms

Lakes in black

Land over 250m

····· Major ice streams radiating
outwards from the Lakeland ice dome

N

The form of glaciated valleys is well known. Frequently referred to as 'U-shaped valleys', few are in fact anything like the letter U in cross section. The valley sides are rarely vertical rock faces, nor are the floors evenly flat. The more descriptive term 'glacial trough' better fits their actual form. They are linear, relatively steep-sided features, deeply eroded into bedrock, but with irregularities both in cross-section and in long profile. The key point in the present context is that their floors have frequently been over deepened by glacial erosion creating enclosed rock basins in which the lakes lie. Only erosion by ice can apparently defy gravity and scoop out large basins of this form in the hard rock of valley floors.

The actual processes involved are quite complex. Glaciers can pull away, pick up and transport bedrock from a valley, often moving it great distances. A process called **'plucking'** (literally quarrying) is the most effective. This involves a glacier removing large chunks and pieces of rock from its bed (Figure 6). Two separate things allow this to take place, the details of which are not entirely understood. First **'fracturing'** of the bedrock takes place and is important in weakening and opening up the rock and breaking it down. Most rocks have naturally occurring weak lines within them – fractures, joints, bedding or cleavage planes etc. and these inherent weaknesses may be sufficient for ice to do its work in breaking material away. In many rocks, however, a more complex positive feedback process may also be at work. As rock is broken away and removed from the uppermost surface of the ground, the natural confining pressure within the lower layers of the rock is released by the removal of the weight above. The rock 'relaxes' or 'unloads' under the pressure release. This particularly occurs in compact igneous rocks. The hard volcanic rocks and granites of central Lakeland, on which many of the big lakes lie, show this feature well. There can thus be a self perpetuating feedback process going on – the more

13

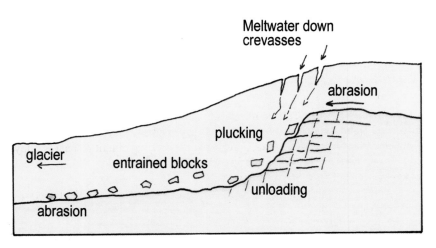

Figure 6.

erosion that occurs, the more the lower layers of rock are relaxed from the confining pressures and the more they are fractured and weakened. Fracturing of bedrock beneath a glacier may also be due to complex patterns of ice pressure. These are transmitted to the underlying bedrock causing stress. It has been shown that stress may be particularly high in cavities in the rock and in the downstream side of rock obstacles, causing big blocks to be fractured and weakened.

The second thing necessary for plucking involves lifting up, pulling away and **'entraining'** pieces of the fractured rock into the basal ice. This may be achieved in a number of ways. Ice may simply freeze to the bedrock, detaching blocks as the ice flows forward. Alternatively, the drag between ice and bedrock may be sufficient to dislodge loose fragments. The inflow of meltwater from crevasses in the ice can also assist this process of removing blocks. Erosion and entrainment of blocks is also linked to the thermal properties of the ice. Some glaciers are 'warm-based', that is the ice is close to the melting point; meltwater is present and consequently the ice is moving over its bed relatively quickly. Lakeland glaciers undoubtedly behaved in this way and such mobile glaciers could achieve high rates of erosion. Once blocks of rock have been plucked from the valley floor and incorporated into the flowing ice at the base of the glacier, they become tools to abrade and scrape the bedrock they pass over. The base of the glacier thus acts like a rough file or piece of coarse sandpaper, wearing away at the valley floor. In volume terms however, abrasion removes far less rock than plucking, but its effects are obvious to see once the ice has melted back. Exposed rock surfaces are left rounded, smoothed and polished.

Several of the big lakes (notably Wast Water, Ennerdale Water, Buttermere, Crummock Water and Bassenthwaite Lake) are contained within single ice excavated rock basins; long linear features in the valley floors, rounded and symmetrical in cross-section but often asymmetrical in long profile. Other lakes, however, are more complex and contain two or more basins (Windermere, Coniston Water and Ullswater). Glaciers do not erode valleys evenly; the processes of plucking, entrainment and abrasion are also governed by the way glaciers behave as they move down a valley. Glaciers flow by a combination of basal sliding and internal deformation. That is, they slide down a valley just like a sledge would move, but at the same time they change their shape as they go (they deform). Flow is broadly driven by gravity as the ice moves downhill under its own weight. In detail, however, flow will vary enormously. The ice will be moving at different rates on the surface and at depth, and will be faster in some sections and slower in others. The ice flows in the direction of the maximum surface slope, even though the bed may be sloping in a different direction. Basal ice can therefore flow uphill in some sections. Bedrock obstacles and changes in gradient of the valley floor all affect flow. There will be longitudinal variations in the velocity of the ice and these will be important in determining where maximum erosion of the valley floor occurs and hence where in the valley a lake basin is excavated.

As a glacier flows down a valley irregularities in the slope of the valley will cause it to develop zones of what is known as **'extending flow'** and **'compressive flow'**. In extending flow the velocity is increasing and the ice is moving towards the bed of the glacier. Within the ice, slip-lines (surfaces along which slipping is taking place), slope downwards towards the bed of the glacier. In compressive flow velocity is decreasing, the ice is being compressed and the slip-lines curve upwards towards the surface (Figure 7C). Ice moving over a slight step in the valley floor will be extending on the up side and over the top of the step, but it will be compressing on the down side in the slight basin below the step. Glacial plucking is very seriously limited in extending flow as bedrock blocks cannot be transported away from the bed, but abrasion will be increased as the contact pressure between the base of the ice and the underlying rock is high. In contrast, plucking is favoured under compressive flow, since loosened blocks can be transported up and away from the base of the ice. The result of this differential erosion is that the basin is deepened and accentuated. This is positive feedback in operation; as the basin is slightly accentuated this will in turn increase the degree of extending and compressive flow in the ice. In this way the basin is deepened at a faster rate than the step is abraded down. (Figure 7).

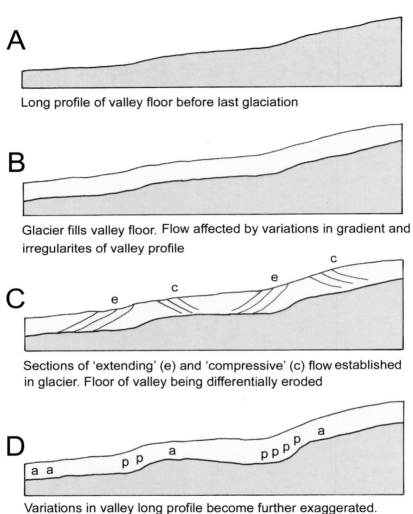

A

Long profile of valley floor before last glaciation

B

Glacier fills valley floor. Flow affected by variations in gradient and irregularites of valley profile

C

Sections of 'extending' (e) and 'compressive' (c) flow established in glacier. Floor of valley being differentially eroded

D

Variations in valley long profile become further exaggerated. Severe erosion by plucking (p) in some sections and lesser abrasion (a) over steps. Unloading of bedrock on valley floor.

E

lake

After glaciation. Ice excavated rock basin now occupied by 'ribbon lake'.

Figure 7. Stages in the excavation of lake basins

THE DEEP POINTS

By looking where the deep points are in the floors of the big lakes it is possible to see where along the main valleys the glaciers were eroding most effectively (Figure 8). In eight of the measured lakes the deepest points are well into the upper half of the lake. In the other four they are close to the mid point. In long profile therefore, the lake basins tend to be slightly asymmetrical, their deepest sections being in the upper reaches. This feature is sometimes referred to as the 'down at heel' profile. Extending this point further, if we consider the twelve separate valleys in which these seventeen big lakes lie, the overdeepened sections are all relatively high up in the valleys, well into the central core of the fells. Only Ennerdale and Wasdale have single deep points in their long profile. All the other valleys have at least two separate rock basins – either as two or more basins within a lake (Windermere, Ullswater, Coniston Water, Esthwaite, Thirlmere and Haweswater), or as separate lake basins (Buttermere/Crummock Water or Derwent Water/ Bassenthwaite Lake). In all these valleys therefore, classic stepped long profiles, sometimes described as 'glacial stairways' are to be found.

It is difficult to be precise in deciding why a lake basin has been created at a particular point within a valley. Initial irregularities in the long profile of the valley floor clearly play a part. These may relate to local geological differences. The situation in Derwent Water for example may relate to this (see later section). The impact of tributary valleys joining a main valley may also be of significance, either in explaining changes in the pre-glacial valley profile or in so far as tributary glaciers contributed more ice in the main valley during glaciation. This situation applied in Ullswater for example (Figure 9).

Figure 9.
The hanging valley of Glencoynedale, Ullswater.
Ice from this tributary valley, joining the main glacier greatly enhanced the capability of the main valley glacier to erode its bed.
The deepest point of Ullswater is in the valley floor just below this junction.

Figure 8.

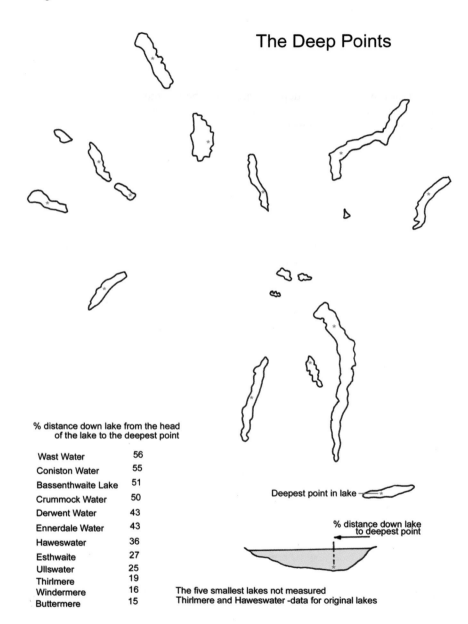

The Deep Points

% distance down lake from the head
of the lake to the deepest point

Wast Water	56
Coniston Water	55
Bassenthwaite Lake	51
Crummock Water	50
Derwent Water	43
Ennerdale Water	43
Haweswater	36
Esthwaite	27
Ullswater	25
Thirlmere	19
Windermere	16
Buttermere	15

Deepest point in lake

% distance down lake
to deepest point

The five smallest lakes not measured
Thirlmere and Haweswater -data for original lakes

DAMMING OF THE VALLEYS

The part damming plays in the forming of the lakes by holding up water in the valley floors and enhancing lake levels is very difficult to ascertain. Glacial moraines and other debris left behind when the ice melted, along with alluvial debris flushed down into the valley floors by streams, undoubtedly exist at the lower end of many of the lakes. Unless we can ascertain how thick such deposits are and whether there are intact bedrock rims beneath actually forming the end of a true ice excavated rock basins, it is impossible to be precise about the extent of damming. What is clear however from detailed examination, is that all the seventeen big lakes lie in rock basins, some have no debris at their lower ends and none of them owe their origin solely to damming. Damming has certainly enhanced the depth of some of the lakes, but everywhere damming takes no more than a minor secondary role in lake formation. The lake basins are all primarily ice excavated features (Figure 10).

The detailed descriptions of the individual lakes in the later sections will elaborate on the particular situations. Extensive moraines are conspicuous at the lower ends of Windermere, Coniston Water and Ennerdale Water and affect the configuration of these lakes (Figures 11 and 12). On the other hand, there is little evidence of any damming of Ullswater, Thirlmere, Grasmere or Rydal Water and minimal evidence at Wast Water or Crummock Water. Brothers Water and Loweswater are however clearly contained by alluvial fans. Fans also separate Derwent Water from Bassenthwaite Lake and Buttermere from Crummock Water, but in all these six cases without the fans there would still be lakes, albeit slightly smaller in area.

Figure 11. Curved boulder clay ridge enclosing end of Ennerdale Water. View from northern Bowness shore of lake, looking west towards outlet.

Figure 10

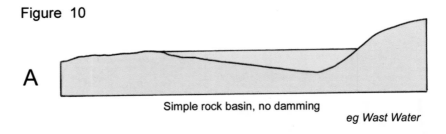

A Simple rock basin, no damming

eg Wast Water

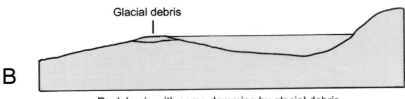

Glacial debris

B Rock basin with some damming by glacial debris

eg Ennerdale Water or Coniston Water

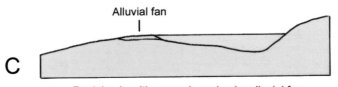

Alluvial fan

C Rock basin with some damming by alluvial fan

eg Brothers Water or Loweswater

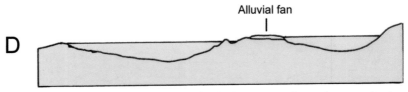

Alluvial fan

D Two separate rock basins with alluvial fan built across rock step between basins

eg Crummock Water / Buttermere
Bassenthwaite Lake / Derwent Water

Figure 12. The Coniston Moraines. A complex series of terminal moraine features surround the outlet of Coniston Water at its southern end near Water Yeat (SD 290895) and High Nibthwaite (SD 294896) and extend up to Park Nab (SD201903).

They clearly hem in the outlet of the lake, but their thickness is unknown. Figure 12a above shows the extreme southern end of the lake with the mounds of the Water Yeat moraine area on the far side of the water. Figure 12b left, shows the hummocky moraine area, again on the Water Yeat side of the lake, but viewed from the south. The lake is not visible from here, but is beyond the fields in the middle distance.

Figure 13. The southern end of Windermere from Gummers How. The River Leven outlet stream turns abruptly SW at the end of the lake and follows the strike of the Silurian rocks. Moraine (M) plugs the lower end of the valley particularly on the eastern side of the lake near Fell Foot.

21

ISLANDS

Islands are significant and noticeable features in eight of the big lakes. In total 46 islands are big enough to bear names. In addition, there are small rocky isles and protruding shoals of rock in almost all the lakes. Only Bassenthwaite Lake, Buttermere, Loweswater and Brothers Water are without islands.

The existence, or indeed absence of islands, reflects geology and the processes that have shaped these basins. In many cases, upstanding hard, rocky protuberances have simply withstood ice erosion and still stand defiantly out from the floors of the valleys. Belle Isle and the numerous rocky lumps between the northern and southern basins of Windermere for example, represent the section of the glacial trough where ice (under extending flow), was moving over a step in the valley profile and failed to obliterate the feature. Similarly, the step in the long profile between the upper and middle reaches of Ullswater is marked by the island of House Holme (Norfolk Island on modern maps). Here tough volcanic rock withstood erosion. Below that point ice, supplemented by a huge glacier tongue joining the valley from Glencoynedale, aided by weaker structures in the rocks (a fault line and beds aligned with the valley direction), was able to sweep the trough clear of obstructions (Figure 9). The middle and lower reaches of the lake being conspicuously free of islands.

Figure 14.
Norfolk Island in Ullswater. A severely ice scoured volcanic rock in mid lake. Looking down lake.

Figure 15.
The neighbouring rocky Wall Holme island in Ullswater. Another protruding island of resistant volcanic rock.

Grasmere has one relatively large rocky island and neighbouring Rydal Water several small irregular rocky islets throughout its length. Here again, ice was unable to sweep the valley floor clear of rocky irregularities. Geology was important here as well; ice was moving across the structural grain of the hard volcanic rocks, particularly at Rydal, and the generally open nature of both basins has left shallow lakes and exposed islands.

The four major lakes without islands (Bassenthwaite Lake, Thirlmere, Haweswater and Buttermere) on the other hand, demonstrate glacial valleys where ice, typically confined by steep mountain sides was able to clear obstructions and excavate simple troughs. Coniston Water, Wast Water and Crummock Water also approach this classic clear trough situation . . . the minute rocky islands there are confined to the extreme flanks of the trough with the centres of the basins being clear, open features. The very deep basin of Wast Water has only one very tiny rock islet right on its SW shore and Coniston Water two small islands, Fir Island and Peel Island tight in the shallows of the eastern shore.

Ennerdale Water presents a very interesting situation. A look at a modern Ordnance Survey map reveals a lake without islands, but surprisingly when lake levels are low the tip of a rocky pinnacle right in the middle of the trough floor emerges as an island (called Little Isle in some references). The present lake level has been slightly raised by a metre or so in order to use the lake as a water supply reservoir.

Figure 16.
below and left.

Little Isle in Ennerdale Water with Anglers' Crag behind is seen in 16a left.

The close up of the pinnacle of Little Isle 16b (right) shows it to have a circular hole in the top. There is some evidence this hole may be artificial.

How this feature survived such deep valley erosion by ice is a problem. Two factors help to explain it. Although it is right in the middle of the lake floor it is at a point towards the lower end of the lake where the valley trough is widening out and the ice was losing the tight confinement between Bowness Knott on the northern side and Anglers' Crag on the south. Perhaps more important however, is the bedrock geology which exposes a particularly hard, resistant stretch of Skiddaw Group rocks which have been hardened by metamorphism near the margin of the adjoining Ennerdale Granite intrusion.

Not all the lake islands are rocky. In Derwent Water the wide shallow basin is dominated at its northern end by the picturesque Derwent Isle, Lords Island, St. Herbert's Island and Rampsholme Island – all oval mounds of glacial till, part of the hummocky drumlin field at the northern end of the lake near Keswick. Similar, drumlin like mounds of glacial till confine the shores of Esthwaite. Only one, Robin Shoals north of Elter Holme on the SE shore stands clear as an island., but two 'near islands', Strickland Ees and Ees Wyke, form striking peninsulas in the lake, not quite cut off as separate entities.

Figure 17. Derwent Water. The drumlin islands at the northern end. The view is from Walla Crag looking north, with Keswick to the right. The view also shows the isthmus separating Derwent Water from Bassenthwaite Lake in the far distance.

FLOATING ISLANDS

Very much a curiosity is the so called 'floating island' that appears periodically in the south east corner of Derwent Water. In hot, dry summers a flat slab of vegetation and mud from the lake bed, buoyed up by methane gas, rises and floats to the surface. It was recorded frequently in the late Nineteenth Century, less so in more recent times. It has varied in size considerably, but was recorded one year at 7500m^2. Particular conditions of shallow water and mats of submerged vegetation seem necessary to produce such features. None of the other lakes have recorded this phenomenon.

LAKE SHORES

Taken together the seventeen big lakes have over 200 kms. of shoreline - certainly much more than that if every minute twist and turn, every bay and promontory and every rocky bump and inlet are measured in detail (Table on next page). The shores not only define the lakes, they convey their characters. It is the shores where most people walk or experience the lakes, where access is gained to the water and where we have an amazing array of extremely diverse types of terrain and different habitats for plants and animals. Many stretches of lake shore present steep rocky crags at the waters edge or smooth platforms of rock, spreads of boulders or scree. Close by we have beaches of sand and pebbles, shorelines of glacial clays and gravels, muddy bays, diverse wetlands, stands of reeds, alder carr and woodlands. Fortunately most of the lakes retain their natural character. The lake shores reflect the bedrock geology and the processes of erosion and accretion that constantly modify their outline. The lake shores are sensitive areas. Habitats are constantly under pressure from erosion, trampling by visitors, use of the lakes for recreation, pollution from lake shore land as well as pressures to build and use them for urban activities.

ROCKY SHORES

Back in the 1920's the eminent biologist and lake researcher W. H. Pearsall produced some figures on the 'rockiness' of the lake shores and the waters at their edges (Table on next page). Whilst this data is not absolutely precise and doesn't convey the full topographical nature of the rocky shores it does draw out the fact that some of these big lakes (notably Wast Water, Ennerdale Water, Buttermere and Crummock Water) are distinctly rocky. On the other hand at the other end of the scale Esthwaite, Elter Water and some sections of other lakes are made up predominantly of soft glacial clays and alluvial materials with few rocky sections. More important than the physical differences is the fact that lakes with rocky shores and rocky catchments are low in biological productivity – rain falling on rocky ground enters the lakes with little in solution. Conversely shores and catchments covered with glacial clays and alluvial deposits generate more nutrients and result in 'productive' rather than 'unproductive lakes'.

Lake	Shoreline length kms.	% of the shoreline rocky
1 Windermere	45.9	28
2 Ullswater	29.3	28
3 Bassenthwaite Lake	20.0	29
4 Derwent Water	13.8	33
5 Coniston Water	19.5	27
6 Haweswater (original lake)	9.0	25
7 Thirlmere (original lake)	10.1	High
8 Ennerdale Water	9.8	66
9 Wast Water	11.1	73
10 Crummock Water	9.6	47
11 Esthwaite	7.0	12
12 Buttermere	5.3	50
13 Loweswater	4.0	Low
14 Grasmere	3.9	25
15 Rydal Water	3.0	Moderate
16 Brothers Water	2.1	Low
17 Elter Water	2.7	Low
Total	206.1	

The shoreline lengths have been measured on 1:25, 000 Ordnance Survey maps and for Thirlmere and Haweswater from earlier OS maps.

The figures for % of the shoreline 'rocky' are from the work of Pearsall (1921) and indicate the rocky nature of the immediate shoreline areas down to a water depth of 9m. Five of the lakes were not measured by Pearsall, estimates of the rocky nature of these lakes has been indicated by the author.

Steep rocky crags front many lake shores. Anglers' Crag (Figure 16a) on the south side of Ennerdale Water is a prominent example. Kailpot Crag, Geordie's Crag and much of the SE shore of Ullswater is also noticeably rocky (Figure 18 and 19).

Figure 18.
Ullswater.
The rocky slopes
of Hallin Fell
plunging steeply
into the lake.
Geordie's Crag is
on right hand end

Figure 19.
below left.
Kailpot Crag (NY
433205). Ullswater.
A steep rocky crag
of volcanic lava
that drops straight
into deep water at
the lake edge.
Below, in the water,
is the Kailpot,
possibly a 'moulin'
feature – a pot hole
less than 1 metre
in diameter that
may have been
produced by
meltwater swirling
down a crevasses
at the edge of
the ice.

Rocky shores of this nature are associated with lake edges that run close to the steep rocky walls of glacial troughs where ice was eroding heavily, hemmed in by steep mountain sides. In other situations, bare rocky shores relate to lower ground where ice overrode and scoured bedrock on the flanks of the valley floors. Hard resistant rock along lake shores often survived erosion and now stands proud as promontories – for example Friars Crag on Derwent Water (a hard intrusion of diorite). Often where the structural grain within a rock (the strike in a rock for example), meets the lake shore at an angle, resistant ribs of rock and promontories extend out from the shores. An example of this is where hard Bannisdale Formation mudstones and sandstones extend out from the eastern shore of Coniston Water at High Peel Near and run through as a ridge along the nearby Peel Island close in shore (SD 295917). Many of the hard rocky shorelines have not altered much since the ice retreated. Wave activity has achieved little erosion, ice smoothed and striated surfaces are still visible near the water's edge (Figure 20) with large erratic boulders left by the ice still in place, too heavy for waves on the lake to move them.

Figure 20.
The western shore of Derwent Water at Brandlehow Park. Ice scoured and striated Skiddaw Group mudstones form the lake shore. Large erratic boulders of volcanic rock carried to the area by ice from the Borrowdale valley lie stranded on the shore.

SCREES

A distinctive type of rocky shoreline exists where rockfalls from steep craggy slopes rising above a lake, produce aprons of scree, often descending to the waters edge and deep below the waterline. Wast Water screes are a classic example, outstanding in the Lake District and probably the best features of this kind anywhere in Britain. Shorter scree shores also exist on Ullswater below Place Fell and on the western shore of Brothers Water and along sections of Thirlmere. Anyone who has walked the Wast Water lake shore path along the foot of the screes will know what a chaotic, awkward jumble of angular rock debris this is …, typically described as *"a dreadful place … avoidable only by a swim in the lake"* by the inveterate Alfred Wainwright in his guide Book to the Southern Fells (1955, Illgill Head 3). On scree slopes a process called fall sorting operates, resulting in the smaller rock fragments staying nearer the top and the largest boulders falling with greater momentum nearer the base. On the Wast Water shore angular boulders well over 1m in size are found. The screes slope steeply (around 30°) down into the lake for another 70m, where much of the debris must be of an even larger size (Figure 21).

SHORELINES OF GLACIAL DEPOSITS

Stretches of shore formed of glacial clays, gravels, moraines and bouldery debris exist in parts of all of these lakes. They dominate the shores of Esthwaite and are prominent along the lower and middle reaches of Ullswater, along many parts of Bassenthwaite Lake and parts of Derwent Water. Soft glacial materials are prone to erosion by wave action. Unlike waves along sea coasts, waves in the lakes clearly are not subject to tidal change and are everywhere far less powerful as erosional agents. The size of the waves in lakes is related to 'fetch' – basically the distance of open water over which wind can generate waves. This is very limited in most lakes and

Figure 21. Wast Water screes

is complicated by shore topography, the orientation and configuration of the shores and the proportions of deep and shallow water. Some shores are more exposed because of their orientation to prevailing westerly and south-westerly winds. Waves are however quite effective in eroding and cliffing these soft shores. Wave action will cut a notch (small cliff) into soft materials.

Figure 22. A soft shoreline on the western side of Crummock Water. The glacial till and alluvial debris has been cut back by wave action. The large pinkish boulders of Ennerdale Granite have been left stranded on the shore.

29

The finer material will be carried away, either washed down into deeper water, or drifted along the shore into quieter bays. Any boulders in the glacial debris will often be too heavy to be moved away and are thus left stranded on the wave washed shore. (Figures 22, 23 and 24)

Figure 23.

The western shore of Derwent Water at Victoria Bay, Old Brandle-how. Shoreline in glacial boulder clay eroded back to notch at base of trees. Abandoned glacial erratics on beach.

Figure 24.

Same site as Figure 23.

Boulder clay platform exposed on beach. Shingle of Skiddaw slate fragments form only thin, incomplete cover over wave cut boulder clay. Large abandoned erratics at back.

Drumlins lie along several lake shores, notably Esthwaite, at the northern end of Derwent Water (Figures 17 and 24) and at the north west corner of Crummock Water (Figure 25) These are frequently cliffed at the shore.

Drumlins and other areas of glacial till produce smooth curved shores, lines of rounded promontories (often in Lakeland called nebs) and gentle bays. The lower reach of Ullswater or the north eastern shore of Bassenthwaite Lake present good examples of this type of shore. (Figure 89)

Figure 25. Broomhill Point, Derwent Water (NY267215)
A cliffed drumlin.
The view on the left above was taken in 1958. The exposed sandy, bouldery till cliff is seen clearly on the left, with a beach below of large boulders derived from the till. The view on the left below is the same location today (taken October 2011). The drumlin is no longer under wave attack and the higher part of the beach is now vegetated over. Because the large boulders from the till are too large for waves to carry them away and they are now so numerous, they are protecting the drumlin face. It is impossible to obtain an exact view from the spot of the 1958 picture because of the dense bushes on the shore area today. The angle of the 2011 picture is slightly different, but the beach is the same.

Figure 26.
Drumlin (centre of picture) at north west corner of Crummock Water (NY151203).
The drumlin is cliffed along most of the shoreline.
The curved bay in the foreground of the drumlin has a fine beach of Skiddaw slate material (see also Figure 37).
The view is from the N. summit of Mellbreak.

DELTAS

Deltas are prominent features in most of the big lakes. Where streams enter lakes their velocity is reduced quite suddenly and the sediment load they are carrying is deposited, progressively building out a new piece of land from the lake shore. A number of quite complex processes are involved in the creation and evolution of deltas. The most important processes relate to the regime of the streams entering the lakes – the amount of water coming in, the size and nature of the catchment of the stream, the amount and calibre of the sediment being carried and the fluctuations in the discharge of the stream. Also of importance is the nature of the lake where a stream enters - its depth, and shape and whether the area is exposed to any currents or prevailing winds. Generally lakes have relatively still water, the velocity of the stream is checked quite quickly, resulting in the coarser sediment being deposited near the shore and the finer material being carried out into deeper water.

Two different types of delta are found in Lakeland's big lakes – so called **lake head deltas** where streams enter a lake at their upper end, and **arcuate deltas** where streams come into the sides of lakes.

Most of the lakes have lake head deltas, but the classic ones are at the head of Wast Water and at the head of Derwent Water. The former is dominated by coarse sediment brought down into the valley head by high-gradient mountain streams, particularly from Lingmell Gill. The main Wasdale Head valley has been progressively infilled by debris brought down Mosedale and Lingmell Becks, but at the lake head these streams, combined with the huge amounts of coarse, angular debris from Lingmell Gill have built up a very large, active delta. Lingmell Gill is prone to high discharges after heavy rain storms, resulting in a constant supply of coarse debris. A further factor affecting the delta here is the fact that the prevailing south westerly winds have a long fetch up the full length of the lake, resulting in erosion of the delta edge and the movement of debris along the impressive delta beach which extends in an arc around the lake head (Figures 27 and 28).

At the head of Derwent Water the lake head delta is a classic bird's foot type. The river Derwent here has a low gradient and is entering a broad shallow lake; as a result, most of the carried sediment is deposited close to the river mouth. The Derwent has a large catchment and carries a relatively high level of small calibre debris. It is called a bird's foot delta because of the way the river channels divide and radiate outwards like the spread of toes on a bird's foot. The sketch in Figure 29 illustrates how this occurs. Basically a bar of debris is deposited at the stream outlet, eventually dividing the water flow

Figure 27. The Wast Water lake head delta seen from the summit of Yewbarrow. Lingmell Gill is at the top of the photo, the main combined channel from Mosedale Beck and Lingmell Beck enters from the left.

Figure 28. Wast Water. The delta shore and beach.

into two separate channels – a process that continues as the delta builds forward, causing repeated bifurcation of the stream channels. At periods of high water the channels will also overflow their banks and build levees (linear banks of coarse deposited debris). Finer debris will be spread thinly over the delta area. Occasionally a break in the wall of the main channel may occur leading to the development of a side channel which will cut through the existing delta spread and find a new outlet – such channels are called 'crevasse splays', but are usually short lived. (Figure 30).

Figure 29

1.

levee

river flow ⟶

'shoal' or
'middle ground bar'
of deposited material at
channel outlet
c = coarse material
f = finer

River flow is deflected into separate
channels either side of shoal

2.

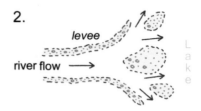

levee

river flow ⟶

Process repeats itself
but now with two
separate channels

Delta builds forward

Figure 30. above: The Derwent Water birds foot delta seen from Surprise
View. The River Derwent enters from the left and now flows through an
extensive delta plain. An old crevasse splay and old delta is indicated by X on
the picture.

Figure 31. The Derwent Water delta in August 1995 at a particularly low water situation. The bare shoals of debris (usually below water level) are well seen. The higher parts of the shoals are now colonised with alder woodland.

Small **arcuate**, or more conventionally D-shaped deltas, occur in almost all the lakes where streams enter from the flanks of the valley. In most Lakeland situations these are steep, high energy mountain streams. Here the deltas produced closely reflect the nature of the debris being brought down by the streams, and in particular they reflect the local geology. An excellent example is at Barrow Beck, Derwent Water – seen in Figure 32 which is also seen from Surprise View (NY 268189) where the contrast with the birds foot delta in Figures 30 and 31 could not be more striking.

Figure 32. above left and right: The Barrow Beck Delta, Derwent Water. (NY 267200). **Left** is seen from Surprise View where the distinct D shape of the feature building out into the lake is very clear. **Right** is a view looking straight down on the delta from the slopes of Brown Knotts.

Nowhere, however, are arcuate deltas illustrated better than in Buttermere where two similar streams on opposite sides of the lake have built very different deltas (Figure 33 and 34).

Figure 33. TWO DELTAS ON BUTTERMERE.

Above: Buttermere, with Crummock Water beyond, seen from Fleetwith Pike. The two deltas building out into Buttermere are shown as C and H.

C is the delta of Comb Beck which descends from the steep slopes of volcanic rocks of Burtness Comb on the left.

H is the delta of Hassnesshow Beck descending from the almost equally steep slopes of Skiddaw Group mudstones and slates on Robinson to the right.

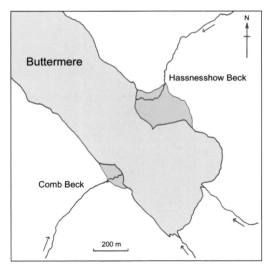

Left: map of the two deltas (in green).

THE TWO BUTTERMERE DELTAS

	Comb Beck	Hassnesshow Beck
Areas of the deltas (kms²)	0.013	0.04
Catchment areas of becks (kms²)	1.076	0.96
Mean slope of the deltas (degrees)	4	2
Mean size of delta material (mm)	25.60	16.51

COMB BECK
Borrowdale Volcanic Group rocks

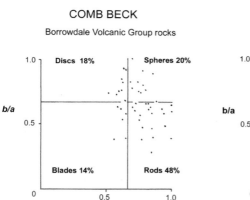

HASSNESSHOW BECK
Skiddaw Group mudstones and slates

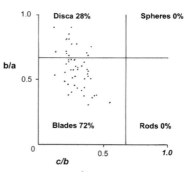

EXPLANATION.

The Hassnesshow delta is more than three times the size of the one at Comb Beck, although Comb Beck has a slightly larger catchment area.

The slope (towards the lake) of the Comb Beck delta is steeper than the Hassnesshow delta.

The scatter diagrams analyse the shape and size of the material making up the deltas. Each dot on the graphs represents a single piece of rock sampled at random from the delta. 50 samples were measured from each delta.

Each piece of rock sampled was measured across three dimensions – its length (a), its thickness (b) and its width (c). The ratios of b/a and c/b were calculated and plotted on the diagrams. This enables each particle to be categorised into four shapes. **Discs** are round, flat pieces (like coins). **Blades** are flat, but long and oval in shape. **Rods** are similar in width and thickness but are long. All three dimensions on **spheres** are similar. The shapes and sizes of the delta material at the two sites clearly reflect the geology. At Hassnesshow the Skiddaw Group rocks are predominantly small discs and blades. At Comb Beck the volcanic rocks produce bigger pieces, that are mainly spheres and rods.

Figure 34. The two Buttermere deltas. Left. Comb Beck is in the fore-ground. Much of it is covered with a plantation of trees. Across the lake, the much larger delta of Hassnesshow Beck has smooth pasture land sloping down to the lake. Note the small spit produced at the prominent southern end of the delta.

Above. Comb Beck delta (with Fleetwith Pike in the background view). Above right the foreshore of the delta with the coarse angular volcanic rock debris.

Above left. Hassnesshow delta, the southern end with spit at the tip (near tree). Above right. The main shore face of the delta consisting of fine flat particles of Skiddaw Group slaty rock. Erosion of the delta face periodically changes the slope and configuration.

There has been some discussion among researchers as to the way streams enter lakes across these arcuate deltas. In many cases, they simply go across the middle of the delta, entering straight into the lake (as at Comb Beck, Buttermere). On the other hand, there does seem to be some evidence that they are more likely to enter the lake on the windward side of the delta (as at Hassnesshow). Deltas protruding out into lakes can be exposed to wave action. On windward sides this can lead to erosion by waves on the delta edge, the dislodged material being drifted along the shore and deposited on the leeward side in quieter water. In some instances small spits are built on the leeward ends as illustrated at Hassnesshow (Figure 34). This idea was first illustrated by Thomas Hay (a local physiographer) on Ullswater in the 1940's, where he initially suggested that streams entered the lake on the up-lake side of deltas. In the case of Ullswater, with prevailing winds blowing from the south west, down the lake would be to windward. The idea does not stand up however when other lakes are examined, there are many examples supporting the idea but many do not.

DELTAS DIVIDING LAKES

Within this group of big lakes there are two classic examples of how deltas have built right across the valley floors from the sides apparently creating two separate lakes. These are Buttermere / Crummock Water and Derwent Water / Bassenthwaite Lake. Two other similar examples on Thirl-mere and Haweswater are unfortunately now largely submerged under the reservoir lakes. In both the former examples, deltaic spreads have built almost level isthmuses of land across shallow steps in the rocky floors of the glacial troughs. Without the delta material, both examples would indeed be continuous stretches of water and appear as single lakes, but in both cases there are separately excavated rock basins in the floor of the glacial trough – just as Windermere has separate north and south basins in its floor today. In Windermere no delta has built up, burying the rocky bar between the basins. In the case of Buttermere and Crummock Water virtually all the delta debris is Skiddaw Group rock material brought down by Sail Beck and Bowder Beck from the north-east side, with very little coming from the opposite slopes. (Again illustrating the different responses of the volcanic and Skiddaw Group rocks we saw at Comb Beck and Hassnesshow).There is a remarkably even and uniform slope of less than one degree across the whole of this delta isthmus. It has been able to pin the outlet stream from Buttermere into Crummock Water to the foot of the steep slope on the opposite side of the valley. At the Crummock Water side of the isthmus there is clearly solid rock just below the surface illustrating a rocky bar between the two lake basins. Nether How (NY 167172) and nearby knolls, and the

Holme Islands in the head of the lake, all outliers of Skiddaw Group rock, clearly illustrate this (Figure 35) **below right.**

The delta isthmus between Crummock Water in the foreground from Buttermere in the distant view.
The material has been derived from the Sail Beck side of the valley (the left). The rocky islands and knolls of the rock bar between the lakes are visible at the head of Crummock Water. The view is from the southern summit of Mellbreak.

A similar picture is found in the even more extensive spread of deltaic material built up between Derwent Water and Bassenthwaite Lake. This has come primarily from the River Greta, but also from Newlands Beck and the other streams from the north western fells on the opposite side of the valley. The picture here is slightly more complicated by spreads of gravel deposits and a series of drumlins which the alluvial material has built around. Again bed rock protrudes through the alluvium at How (NY 247243) and at Hodgson's How (NY 245236), confirming a step in the trough floor.

Figure 36.

The isthmus between Derwent Water (left) and Bassenthwaite Lake (in the distance).

Keswick is on the right of the picture.

View is from the slopes of Bleaberry Fell.

The original outlines of both Thirlmere and Haweswater show deltas building across the middle of the lakes, from Middlesteads and Thrang Gills on Thirlmere (Figure 91) and from Measand Beck on Haweswater (Figure 102).

BEACHES

Beaches exist in the lakes where sediment (sand, gravel and cobbles) has been allowed to accumulate usually in bays or on protected stretches of shore behind promontories. The material making up the beaches very much reflects the debris available from the breakdown of the local bedrock or the sediments brought down into the lakes by streams or washed from the surrounding slopes. Consequently we don't find fine sandy beaches as on our sea coasts. Typically lake shore beaches are gravelly, stony or formed of thin flaky particles, the material that the local rocks provide. Undoubtedly the best beaches lie on the lake shores underlain by the slaty Skiddaw Group rocks – notably on Crummock Water, Buttermere, Derwent Water and Bassenthwaite Lake. Here the slate has been broken down to small disc like fragments, easily moved, rounded and washed by the waves. The Silurian rocks of south Lakeland produce some similar beaches on Coniston Water and Windermere. On the volcanic rocks of central Lakeland coarser, gravelly beaches characterise Ullswater, Thirlmere, Haweswater and the smaller Grasmere, Rydal Water and Brothers Water.

Figure 37.
Beach near Highpark at the NW corner of Crummock Water.

A curved stretch of remarkably well sorted, mainly Skiddaw Group slaty beach material (inset, top left). The material is contained between a drumlin in the foreground and a further bank of glacial boulder clay on the far side, at the foot of the steep slopes of Mellbreak. Storm waves move the material up and down the beach.

Many of the bay beaches change little in extent, but there is constant movement of material up and down the beaches. Winter storms and periods of high water level carry material up the beaches building storm ridges, often high above normal water levels. In quieter times, wave action combs down the material back into shallow water. One effect of this is to sort beach material, the larger pieces being pushed to the top of the beach under high wave action and abandoned there.

At Low Ling Crag on the western shore of Crummock Water there is an interesting beach feature, the only one of its kind in the Lake District (Figure 38). Two curved gravel beaches tie a small glacially smoothed rocky island in the lake to the lake shore. This kind of feature is known as a **tombolo**.

Figure 38. Low Ling Crag. Crummock Water (NY156184).

Left: Looking down on the feature from Mellbreak.

Below **left** and **right:** the north and south beaches respectively.

The beach material of well-sorted, medium gravel, mostly of Skiddaw Group slaty fragments has accumulated in a 60m long strait between the shore and the island and has been shaped by waves into two curved beaches facing north and south. A slight grassy depression lies between the two ridges of beach material. The north facing (down lake) beach frequently shows several steep **berm** ridges in cross beach profile. These are usually associated with exposed beaches, where constructive waves can push material up beach and create steep fronts in the gravel. Prevailing winds on Crummock Water tend to be coming up the valley. A comparison of the beach material measured on the two beaches by the author does illustrate some differences between the two sides of the feature. The mean size of the gravel (average of the length, width and thickness of each particle) on the north side (15.7 mm) is very slightly larger than the south beach (14.8 mm). On both beaches however the shape of the gravel is very similar with virtually all the particles being disc or blade shaped.

SPITS AND THE DRIFTING OF MATERIAL ALONG SHORES

On sea coasts waves breaking obliquely on shores and powerful currents offshore, move beach material along shorelines and construct complex spits, bars and ridges. Such action in our lakes is very limited. We have seen that on some deltas wave action will carry material away and redeposit it on lee shores. There are a few examples of walls and groynes on the lake shores trapping drifting sediment on one side – for example on the eastern end of the beach at Sandwick, on Ullswater (NY 425200). There are also some examples of small spits on deltas (eg Hassnesshow on Buttermere Figure 34) One is building out from the inlet of Park Beck into the north-east corner of Crummock Water (Figure 39). Interestingly there are northerly pointing spits attached to the north-east corners of both St. Herbert's Island and Rampsholme Island in Derwent Water, indicating a northerly drift of sediment towards the outlet end of the lake. (Figure 40). *(Both are well seen on Google Earth)*.

Figure 39.

Spit building out from the mouth of Park Beck where it enters Crummock Water near its northern end. The spit is being deflected north-wards by the drift of water towards the outlet of the lake in the far distance

Figure 40.

Spit projecting northwards from the northern tip of Rampsholme Island on Derwent Water.

WETLANDS

Many low lying shore areas are fringed with wetland habitats. They occur particularly along shorelines that are not exposed to wind and waves. Thus they are frequently found where sediments are infilling the heads of the lakes or in shallow bays where streams enter. Classic examples occur at the heads of Esthwaite, Derwent Water and Bassenthwaite Lake, or in quiet bays like Pull Wyke on Windermere, Fold Yeat on Esthwaite or Thwaitehill on Ullswater. They are also features of some of the smaller lakes which tend to be shallow and sheltered – Elter Water, Rydal Water or Brothers Water.

The ecology of many of these Lakeland wetlands is known in some detail, largely through the research work of the Freshwater Biological Association which for many years has had its headquarters on Windermere. Several sites are of international importance for their plant and animal life. Wetlands are delicately balanced habitats. They are environments that are sensitive to human interference and pollution, sensitive to changes in water chemistry, silting and sediment deposition, natural erosion and the cycles of vegetation growth and decay. These Lakeland wetlands possess distinctive structures and present striking differences in plant assemblage in any transect from open lake water up on to drier land where they merge into other plant communities. Many have classic **hydroseres** – plant successions that progressively build out into the lake and convert a water body to a land community. As plants die back each year their remains accumulate. Sediment is trapped and consolidated. Plants loving drier conditions can gradually encroach into what was once a water environment.

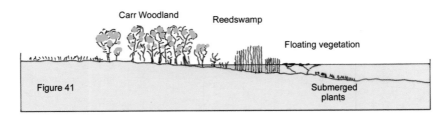

Carr Woodland   Reedswamp

Floating vegetation

Figure 41

Submerged plants

Figure 41 shows a typical hydrosere succession on these wetland shores. Vegetation can only survive in open lake water where light can penetrate. The mosaic of plants that are found reflects the complex balance between local variations in depth, wave action, substrate, silting and the composition of the water. Quilwort *(Isoetes lacustris)*, a small (8-25 cm) rosette plant with spikey, quill like leaves, will grow on stony areas which are kept free of silt and dead plant debris. Shoreweed *(Littorella)* can withstand wave action, whereas Stonewort *(Nitella)* prefers silty substrates. For these com-

44

pletely submerged plants the ultimate limiting factor is the depth of light penetration. In depths up to 3m floating leaved plants with flexible stalks such as water lilies and some Pondweeds *(Potomogeton sp.)* can root themselves on the lake bottom and survive in quiet water. Further into the shallow water reedswamps appear. Commonly on these big lakes it is the Common Reed *(Phragmites communis)* that is dominant. Standing in water up to a metre in depth it can reach 3m in height and usually forms pure stands. It can produce large amounts of vegetative debris and is an effective sediment trap. On the landward side the pure stands of reeds merge into more diverse plant communities. Other types of reed and the Bullrush may be present, but marsh plants will dominate, commonly Bottle Sedge *(Carex rostrata)*, Water Horsetail *(Equisetum fluviatile)* and numerous other mosses, rushes and small wet habitat plants. Over time rhizomes knit the soil together. Above water, leaves transpire moisture and leaf litter accumulates. The soil becomes suitable for the invasion of herbs and gradually marsh vegetation begins to disappear. Progressively trees, particularly willows and alder will colonise and produce what is commonly known as carr woodland.

Figure 42. The shore of Loweswater near Hudsons Place (NY 118220). Floating pads of water lilies (Nymphaea alba) in the foreground, behind stands of bulrush (Scirpus lacustris). Carr woodland further along shore.

Figure 43. Wetland shores.

Left: Classic hydrosere at the head of Esthwaite.

Reed swamps of *Phragmites communis* circle the head of the lake with alder and willow carr behind.

Reedswamps

Reedswamps and Alder Carr – Bassenthwaite Lake

Alder Carr – Elter Water

LAKE SEDIMENTS

Lying at the bottom of the lakes at the present day is all the debris that has been accumulating ever since the basins were created by the ice. How much material is there, and how far below that is the solid rock, is difficult to ascertain. There is certainly sedimentary debris of one kind or another on all the lake floors. In Windermere, the longest of the basins, and the only one that has been investigated in any detail, the debris is over 20m thick in the North Basin and nearly twice that in the South Basin. Estimates of the depth to the solid rock beneath range up to minus 120m below sea level. What lies on the lake floors however, provides a record of what has been happening to our landscapes since the ice disappeared. The sediments are like a diary of events, with distinct time lines recording changes, layer upon layer of whatever finds its way into the water and sinks to the bottom.

There are two ways of investigating the sediments on the floors of the lakes. The best and most commonly applied method is by coring. A device, rather like drainpipe is driven into the lake bed to extract a section through soft sediments. This is not a simple technique and it has the disadvantage that it can normally only penetrate down 5 or 6 metres or so. The second way is by seismic surveying, essentially measuring the sediment infill using echo sounding. This is expensive and has really only been employed in Windermere in the Lake District. Evidence from these methods however, has shed a great deal of light on the history of these big lake basins. Figure 44 is a diagrammatic representation of the lake bed sediments, their succession and the time lines within them. It is based primarily on the data available from Windermere, but similar successions must exist in the other large basins, although they have not been explored in anything like the same detail.

Once the erosion of ice had done its work in excavating the rock basins and the melting and wasting away of the ice had begun, the process of infilling the basins with debris took place almost simultaneously. The ice occupying the basin would itself have contained rock debris and had glacial till at its base – this would immediately have been released by the ice and simply came to rest in the basins – probably at the same time as the water was beginning to accumulate and before we could really describe these features as lakes. In all these big lakes the deposits lying at the bottom on the rock floor are masses of bouldery material, cobbles, gravels and clays that simply melted out of the ice. These usually grade upwards into sandy material and finer clays that were washed in by meltwaters. All this lower infill is difficult to core and in most of the big lakes is of unknown thickness. On top of this jumble of sediments coring of Windermere shows a series of very regular, alternating bands of laminated clays up to 15m in total thickness. The bands average 2 cms thick at first, but get thinner towards the top of the pile, where they are barely 3 mm thick. This banding is interpreted as representing seasonal accumulations. The surrounding landscape around the lake still contained ice, everything during the winter months was still frozen and hence for long periods each year, little material was being delivered into the lake. In the milder summer months however, sediment found its way into the lake – coarse sandy particles settling out quickly on the bottom, the finer clay material taking longer and settling out more slowly, hence giving the pile a laminated appearance. The annual layers are called **varves** and can be counted just like tree rings as time markers. Their upper boundary marks the end of the glacial period.

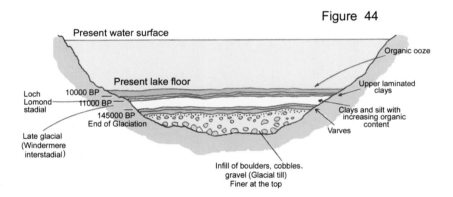

Figure 44

Lake floor sediments
Diagrammatic - not to scale
Based on available data, mainly from Windermere

Progressively as the climate ameliorated and winter conditions became less severe, the seasonal pattern of debris accumulation became less evident, marked in the core records by continuous clay deposits. The ice left a bare, open, rugged landscape devoid of vegetation but susceptible to erosion by slope wash and streams. Much inorganic debris – silt and clay thus found its way into these lakes and down to the lake floor. Gradually however, as vegetation took a hold on the landscape, with mosses and alpine species at first, then later, grasses, shrubs and trees, the natural accumulation on the lake floors changed. Noticeably its organic content increased, but with the stabilisation of the slopes by vegetation its volume decreased.

It is the organic content of the debris that has enabled the history of events to be unlocked. Diverse assemblages of plant and animal remains are preserved in these lake floor sediments. By a variety of sophisticated scientific techniques, minute remains can be identified and dated. Radio-carbon dating, analysis of pollen remains, microscopic analysis of diatoms and the deciphering of amazingly small fragments of such things as beetles, skeletal fragments of midges and small crustaceans have enabled detailed pictures of events to be built up. A consistent increase in organic content of the sediments continued as the landscape became completely colonised by vegetation and the fauna diversified. By about 12,200 BP signs of change are recorded in the sediments with an increased rock content implying erosion of the landscape. Plant and animal remains become less abundant. The climate was cooling. Between 11,000 and 10,000 BP the sediments record a further series of varved clays; 400 or so in Windermere. The landscape had sunk into a 'mini ice age' (The Loch Lomond Stadial). We know from landform evidence small glaciers re-appeared in Lakeland, probably for no more than 500 years.

After that, progressively the climate ameliorated and by 10,000 years ago the small glaciers had disappeared, since when, Lakeland has been ice free to the present day. In the lake floor sediments the last 10,000 years is recorded by a pile of brown organic rich mud. Right at the top of the pile is a veneer of black ooze – the debris (mostly organic) that has fallen to the lake floor in very recent years and is continuing to do so to the present day.

ARE THE LAKES FILLING IN?

The straight answer to this question is clearly yes. Providing conditions stay more or less as they are at present and we have no dramatic geological changes (which seems unlikely in the immediate future), all the big lake basins in the Lake District will eventually fill up with sediments and disappear as landscape features. We have seen in earlier sections how material is being carried into the lakes by streams and how it is washed or falls into lakes from surrounding slopes and how deltas are being built out from lake shores. Our knowledge of the floors of the lakes tells us that a lot of debris has already accumulated there. When we come to face the wider questions however of how long it will take for the lake basins to fill up, or how much sediment and debris is going into the lakes at present, the answers become more difficult. A number of very complex processes of lake infilling are going on. It is not just a question of knowing how old the rock basins are (a question we can answer fairly accurately), measuring how much infill we have got so far (a far more difficult calculation) and then extrapolating out when in the future these basins will be full.

A number of points are critical in understanding this issue of lake infilling. First and foremost it is what is happening in the catchment area of a lake that will determine how the lakes will infill. The size of the catchment, its underlying geology, its topography, vegetation cover and land use and its climatic regime will all affect the amount of material being transported and deposited in the lake. The table below illustrates the huge variation in the present catchment areas of the big lakes – a very important factor in determining the amount of sediment being delivered into the basins.

	Surface area of lake kms²	Catchment area kms²
Windermere	14.76	230.5
Ullswater	8.94	145.5
Derwent Water	5.35	82.7
Bassenthwaite Lake	5.28	237.9
Coniston Water	4.91	60.7
Haweswater (original lake)	1.38	29.1
Thirlmere (original lake)	1.34	29.3
Ennerdale Water	2.99	44.1
Wast Water	2.91	48.5
Crummock Water	2.52	43.6
Esthwaite	1.0	17.1
Buttermere	0.94	16.9
Grasmere	0.64	27.9
Lowes Water	0.64	13.9

There is no relationship between the present size of the lakes and their catchment area. Bassenthwaite Lake for example, has a large catchment area, larger than Windermere, but it has two other large lakes within its system. On the other hand Thirlmere and Haweswater (both water supply reservoirs) have small catchments for their size. Grasmere, one of the smallest lakes, has a relatively large catchment.

Sediment on the floors of the lakes is not distributed evenly. It is noticeably thicker in deeper water and varies greatly from one part of a lake to another. What this demonstrates is that once silt, sand and larger particles, as well as organic debris, gets into the water it is moved around before it settles on the lake floor. Moreover, once it has settled it may then be further disturbed, taken back into suspension or moved somewhere else by waves and currents. Processes, sometimes known as **sediment focusing** therefore operate, whereby sediment can be concentrated or distributed to certain parts of the lake floor. We have seen how with a stream entering a lake the coarser particles will be deposited close to the lake edge as the energy flow is quickly dissipated and a delta will be created. The fine material however will be carried well out into the lake by a river plume where it may be deposited or may be continuously mixed into the entire volume of lake water. This mixing process has been shown to be very complex. In the bigger lakes seasonal temperature changes occur, leading to mixing of the water. Sediment traps placed at various positions on the lake floors not only record differences at different depths, but differences at different times of the year. Shore lines come within wave attack moving material from one place to another and re-suspending particles into the water. Heavy rain storms wash particles straight off slopes into the water where they are carried away. Critically therefore, sediment suspended in the water and mixed throughout the lake will cause more sediment to come to rest where the water is deep. This is simply because there are more sediment particles in a column of deep water – their mass is a linear function of depth. Lakes therefore fill up primarily from the bottom upwards, they become shallower over time and tend to retain their surface area. Deltas are building out from the sides, but they can only go out so far into deep water, far more important in lake infill is the build up of material from the floor upwards.

A further very important consideration is that the volumes of material going into these big lake basins since the last ice age when they were created has varied enormously over time. It is far less now than it was at times in the past. When we look at the amount of sediment being carried by streams today and calculate how much material has already accumulated in deltas and alluvial fans in the valley floors in the last 14,500 years or so since the last ice age, the sums just don't add up. In order to have accumulated so much debris, streams in the past must have been carrying far more debris than they do at present. Undoubtedly the volumes carried down into the valley floors in the first few thousand years after the ice disappeared were enormous. This is a reflection of the large volumes of loose material that the melting ice sheets left behind and the fact that the landscape was not stabilised with a vegetation cover. Another significant change over time that must also be remembered is that the chemistry of the lake waters has changed, this has resulted in changes to the organic content of the sediments. The biological productivity of the lakes was different in the early stages when soluble bases from the rocks were available to be leached into lake waters.

The right kind of data is simply not available to calculate the likely life span of the existing big lakes with any precision. In human terms we must be looking at enormous lengths of time, measured in tens and hundreds of thousands of years before the lakes will be infilled. In Windermere we know that the post-glacial sediments of the last 10,000 years are c.5m thick in the North Basin and only c.3m thick in the South Basin. This suggests a mean rate of accumulation of only 0.3-0.5 mm per year. Taking the big lakes overall the maximum depth of these post-glacial sediments is only between 3 and 6m. (The post-glacial sediments it must be remembered represent only the topmost layer of what is there at the bottom of the lakes – Figure 44, but they are the most relevant to our question). There is strong evidence that the rates of infill have been accelerating a little over very recent historical time – certainly in the last 150 years with changes in agricultural practice and environmental impacts attributable to man. Nevertheless infill rates are incredibly slow.

Even extrapolating these crude figures gives numbers in the tens of thousands of years, but the number of possible variables in such calculations makes them inconclusive. As was emphasised earlier it is what is happening in the catchments that will determine how quickly the lakes will fill in. The more friable and fissile Skiddaw Group rocks, as we have seen from the data on deltas, would seem to suggest lakes on those rocks would fill more quickly. The shallow, productive lakes like Esthwaite or Elter Water will see accelerated change because of man made change, as compared with the rocky, unproductive lakes of say Wast Water or Ennerdale Water. Small, shallow lakes with large catchments such as Grasmere must also have a higher potential to infill.

FORMER BIG LAKES?

One final question remains in this discussion on lake sediments and infilling. Do any former lake basins exist that have already been infilled ? In the discussion on the pattern of lakes in the radial valleys of Lakeland at the beginning of the book, the lack of big lake basins in Eskdale, Dunnerdale, Great Langdale and Longsleddale was alluded to. Ice considerably modified all of these valleys, all of them acted as conduits for ice emanating from the central core of the Lakeland fells and conditions must have been similar in these valleys to the ones where we now have big lakes today. Perhaps just local differences in the severity of ice erosion or geological and topo-graphical factors may account for the dissimilarities.

The evidence we have is inconclusive. There are certainly flat valley floors that may be beds of former lakes in Great Langdale, Longsled-dale and in a section of mid-Eskdale. In upper Borrowdale and in Patterdale (above Ullswater) possible lake beds need investigating. In Great Langdale there is a continuous spread of alluvium across the flat valley bottom from the area close to the junction of Mickleden and Oxendale for almost 5 km down valley as far as the Chapel Stile area (NY 315055). All of this land lies around the 90-95m OD mark and is exceedingly flat in certain sections. The valley floor has certainly been infilled with alluvial debris, but it is possible this is the product of fluvial activity in the valley floor rather than material that has been washed into standing lake water. Until the sediments can be analysed at depth and some picture obtained of the configuration of the rock floor beneath, we cannot be sure whether a lake existed. There is no evidence of a moraine at the lower end of the valley that could have contained a lake, but there is a rocky bar in the valley profile here. The situation in Longsleddale is rather different. It is possible to see four separate former lake basins strung out like a string of beads along the valley floor from just above Sadgill (NY 480074) down to Garnett Bridge. Again however, the sediments in the basins have not been demonstrated as being lacustrine, but there are clear rock bars across the valley floor below each section. Old lake beds in Upper Borrowdale and Patterdale do appear to be impounded behind terminal moraines but they are probably of a later date than the Main Glaciation. In mid Eskdale the valley floor areas are irregular and the infill may be fluvial in origin and not representing an old lake basin. Dunnerdale is even more irregular and old lake beds of any size do not appear to have been produced. Both Eskdale and Dunnerdale are rather open glacial troughs with the ice probably less confined between steep walls as in other Lakeland valleys, ice had relatively free egress from the these troughs out south westwards into the Irish Sea ice and over the relatively low interfluve areas.

Figure 45. Possible old lake bed in the upper part of Borrowdale. View from near Thorneywaite Farm looking up valley towards the fell of Base Brown.

THE INDIVIDUAL LAKES

In this final section of the book, some illustrations, maps and short descriptions of the 17 individual lakes are presented. A standard format for all the maps has been adopted and the key is shown below. Because of the huge variation in the sizes of the lakes it is impossible to present the maps at a uniform scale. The bathymetric contouring detail also varies between the lakes – only selected contours are shown. Because of space constraints it is also inevitable that the levels of detail on the maps will vary. The 1:25,000 Ordnance Survey Explorer Maps (OL 4, 5, 6 and 7) are the indispensible guides to the locational details when looking at these lakes at first hand.

KEY TO LAKE MAPS

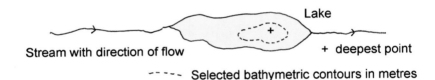

Lake

Stream with direction of flow   + deepest point

----- Selected bathymetric contours in metres

 Rock. Rocky crags and fellside slopes where bedrock is at, or close to the surface.

 Superficial glacial deposits.
Mostly boulder clays, but also glacial sands and gravels

 Alluvium
Deltas, fans and valley floor spreads of alluvium.

Wetlands

↑N Most of the maps are conventionally orientated with north at the top. The map for Wast Water is tilted slightly.

Note : the scale of the maps varies from lake to lake.

WINDERMERE

From Sour Howes looking south

**I overlooked the bed of Windermere,
Like a vast river, stretching in the sun.
With exultation, at my feet I saw
Lake, islands, promontories,
   gleaming bays,
A universe of Nature's fairest forms ...**

William Wordsworth
'The Prelude' iv, 1-5

If you take the Lake Cruise along the length of Windermere from Ambleside to Bowness and then down to Lakeside near the outlet, as many thousands do almost every day of the year, you can gain a real appreciation not just of the sheer size of this lake, but of its character. At 17 km long and with an area of 15 km^2 it is not only Lakeland's largest lake, but England's largest. In reality it feels like two lakes for its North and South Basins are quite distinct, separated by the relatively narrow, shallow section near Bowness where numerous islands obscure the view between the two. In fact, on your Lake Cruise you may well have to change boats at Bowness and do the two sections independently. Maps of the lake are frequently split into two halves – as I have had to do in this book. It can, as Wordsworth felt, seem like a vast river stretching across the landscape. The view of the lake from the water reveals its landscape character. This is 'upland' rather than 'mountainous Lakeland'; strikingly wooded on both its shores. The quiet western shore contrasts heavily with the development on the eastern side with its marinas, hotels, boat houses, piers, lavish houses and straggling urbanisation.

The North Basin is distinctly wider and deeper than the rather longer South Basin. It has been calculated that the North Basin contains just over 60% of the volume of water in the whole lake. It reaches a depth of 64m with steeply shelving shores, particularly on the western side below the steep, wooded slopes of Claife Heights (Figures 46 and 48c). The submerged rocky step between the two basins is an irregular area of islands and shallow waters less than 5m deep. Belle Isle is the largest island, but 12 others in the same area are large enough to have names. There are numerous other smaller rocks and shoals in the shallow waters (Figure 50). The South Basin has a maximum depth of 42m with the steepest shores on the eastern side where Gummers How (321m) is the dominant fell (Figure 48). The lake surface lies at 39.3m so the deepest areas of both basins lie below sea level – emphasising the power of ice to excavate deep rock basins. As we have seen in earlier sections considerable thicknesses of glacial and alluvial debris lie on the floor of the lake, the actual rockhead, according to some estimates, being as deep as minus 120m below sea level.

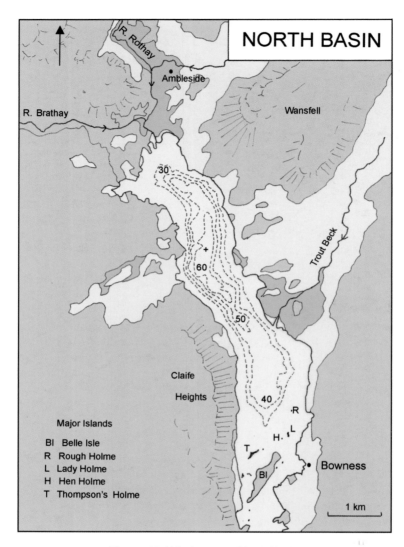

Figure 46. Windermere: North Basin

A typical section through the Windermere lake floor sediments was shown in Figure 44. Some very recent research published in 2010 using high-resolution seismic equipment has not only produced more data on the stratigraphic succession in these deposits but has provided a better picture of the history of events regarding the erosion and filling of the basin. In the thick glacial debris at the very base of the deposits 16 separate moraines have been distinguished, representing stages in the retreat of the glacier up the lake northwards. There is a greater infill of material in the South Basin. The reason for this is that in the final stages of the ice melt finer deposits were being washed from the North Basin over the rocky sill between the two basins. In addition, material was being washed into the South Basin from the wasting Esthwaite glacier to the west. In the uppermost layers of the sediments evidence of a series of flow events in the material is seen. These relate to the time when there was a temporary re-advance of glacial conditions between 11.7 and 12.9k BP. Debris was moving and falling along the lake floor and wet debris was landsliding from the slopes of the basin. In the North Basin slope failure deposits moved from Claife on the western shore into the deep part of the basin. In the South Basin there were similar slope failure movements from both sides. It is this new work that is suggesting that the rockhead on the floor of the trough may be as deep as minus 120m below sea level – much deeper than previous estimates.

Figure 47. The high volcanic fells surrounding the northern end of the lake – the Langdale Pikes at the extreme left across to Fairfield and the fells above Troutbeck at the right.

The glacier that carved out the Windermere basin was a large one, being fed by major feeder glaciers from Great Langdale, the Rothay, Rydal, Scandale, Stock Ghyll and Troutbeck valleys, all of which emanated from the high volcanic fells of SE Lakeland at the northern end of the lake. Ice from the tongue that cut Esthwaite to the west supplemented the Windermere ice stream in the South Basin. The line of the lake cuts across the geological structural lines. The 'upland' character of the shores and fells is due to the fact that this is the area of Silurian rocks that dominate the southern third of the Lakeland massif (Figure 4). These rocks do not produce high fell country. The lake shores are cut across hard slates, mudstones, sandstones and siltstones. Harder beds frequently stand out as promontories and smaller headlands, weaker beds have been worked back into bays. All the strata strike SW-NE across the lake. Promontories like Wray Crag (NY 377015) (hard calcareous siltstones of the Coldwell Formation) or Storrs Temple (NY 391942) (steeply dipping banded siltstones of the Bannisdale Formation) are good examples of resistant features. At Pull Wyke (NY 365022) in the northwest corner the muddy rocks of the Brathay Formation have proved weak and form a bay.

Figure 48. a. Windermere looking north from Gummers How.
b. The steep slopes of Gummers How seen from the lake (looking south).
c. The steep wooded slopes of Claife Heights on the western shores of the North Basin.

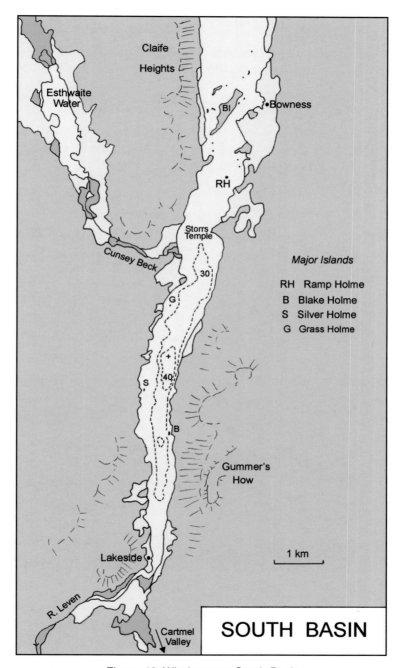

Figure 49. Windermere: South Basin

The area of the outlet from the lake at the southern end is particularly interesting. The River Leven takes a sharp bend at the exit of the lake, flowing south-westwards in a deeply cut rock gorge which follows the strike and structural alignment of the Bannisdale Formation rocks. Around the low-lying shores of the outlet (particularly on the eastern bank) some distinctive morainic mounds can be seen (Figure 13). These do not, however, seem to constitute a morainic dam to the water. Some time ago it was suggested that these moraines may be plugging an old, southerly trending former outlet of the lake that went due south into the Cartmel valley. Seismic investigations of this valley in 1947 proved inconclusive, but more recent investigations in 1987 proved there is a rocky bar across this valley and that it is not plugged with glacial debris. The bar lies 21m above lake level, proving that the existing River Leven outlet is an early feature.

Windermere does not have many particularly low lying stretches of lake shore. Rocky promontories, bouldery shores, narrow beachs and shallow bays plastered with glacial boulder clays form much of the waterfront. The River Rothay has built alluvium into the head of the lake, much of it fringed with wetland. The Trout Beck coming into North Basin has the largest arcuate delta area and again much of it along the lake shore is wetland. Boulder clays along the shores are more widespread along the southern shores, where some gently sloping pasture land fronts the lake.

Figure 50.
The islands in the middle reach of Windermere – view looking north.
Hen Holme (left), Lady Holme (right). Rough Holme
(further right in the distance).

GRASMERE and RYDAL WATER

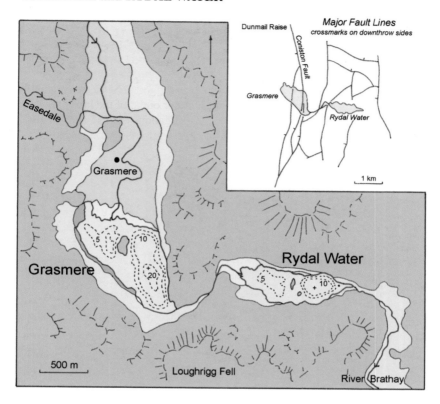

Figure 51. Grasmere and Rydal Water

The neighbouring lakes of Grasmere and Rydal Water lie in an area of very complex volcanic rocks, well within the fells of SE Lakeland. Hard, resistant lavas and volcanic ash deposits, cut by important fault structures were selectively eroded by ice in this area, many offering great resistance to the erosive forces. The topography is complex and intricate. A major fault line (the Coniston Fault), slices N-S through central Lakeland. Thirlmere is aligned along it; southwards it comes along the line of Dunmail Raise and into the basin that Grasmere now occupies (Figure 51 inset). It then strikes southwards and extends down to Coniston. Similar parallel N-S fault lines run down the Rydal Beck valley towards Ambleside and cut across the eastern end of Rydal Water. Other structures within the rocks, notably the way the beds are inclined, run W-E. Again, this affected the way ice eroded the area. Grasmere is aligned with the N-S structures – Rydal Water is controlled more by the W-E grain. Both lakes are relatively shallow and

61

irregular, both have rocky sections along their shores and both have rocky islands which can all be accounted for by the intricacies of the geology. Even the main A591 road, which links these two lakes, is controlled by this geological configuration – running W-E along the northern side of Rydal Water, then, making an abrupt change of direction to run N-S along the eastern side of Grasmere. At the lower (eastern) end of Rydal Water, the River Rothay and the valley alignment reverts immediately to the N-S structural line, falling southwards towards Ambleside.

Grasmere has two distinct basins, either side of the prominent rocky island that dominates the lake (Figure 52 left). The eastern basin reaches 21.5 m deep, far deeper that the smaller western part which reaches 10 m. Grasmere was excavated by ice coming south from a group of valleys north-west of the basin (Greenburn, Easedale and Far Easedale). A tongue of ice was forced eastwards to cut Rydal Water, but much of the ice stream overtopped the Loughrigg Fell ridge to the south, joining the Great Langdale glacier. There is a considerable area of alluvial infill on the valley floor north of the present lake. The village of Grasmere stands on it, but several rocky knolls, notably Butterlyp How, stand proud of the valley floor and indicate solid bedrock is not far below the present valley floor. The River Rothay enters the lake through a wetland delta area. The main current of water from the Rothay into the lake, seems to run to the east of the island and down to the outlet at the SE corner. A very small weir has been constructed here to stabilise the level of the lake.

(Figure 53 right)

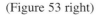

Figure 54. Grasmere, looking north towards Dunmail Raise from Loughrigg Terrace. The exit of the River Rothay from the lake is over the small weir at the bottom right (seen in closer view in Figure 53)

Rydal Water is quite an irregular lake, with low rocky peninsulas and ribs of rock running into the water, two significant rocky islands, numerous isolated rocky islets, soft bays based on glacial boulder clay deposits and extensive wetland areas at its western end. The floor of the lake is irregular. At the western end the basin is shallow reaching only 8m, but a deeper basin of 19m occurs at the eastern end. There is also a considerable thickness of organic sediment in the floor of the basins. Much of the mineral sediment is probably trapped and retained in Grasmere. Rock is seen in the bed of the Rothay where it exits the lake, there is no evidence of morainic damming.

Figure 55. Rydal Water looking eastwards from Loughrigg Terrace.

ELTER WATER

Elter Water is the smallest and shallowest of these 17 big lakes. It also has the most unusual shape, really three almost separate stretches of water joined together via narrow straits in a sort of double dumb-bell arrangement. Clearly it used to be much larger than it is at present with extensive shallows around its shores and low lying marsh and wetlands on almost all sides. It is unobtrusive in the landscape, a secretive kind of lake, largely because it is difficult to see, difficult to access and always seemingly out of view behind trees, reedswamps and vegetation.

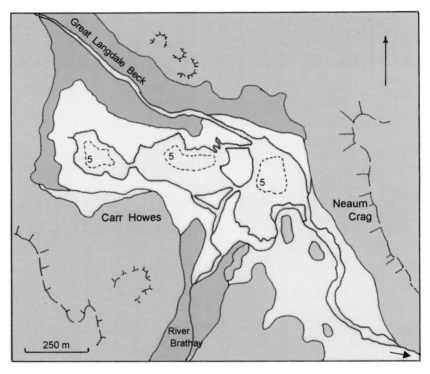

Figure 56. Elter Water

It lies in the lower part of Great Langdale, really at its junction with Little Langdale; much of the lake being where the River Brathay (from Little Langdale) comes into the main valley to join the Great Langdale Beck. Both streams have large catchments. The underlying volcanic bedrock has little bearing on the form of the lake as the valley floor is thickly plastered with glacial till and alluvium. There was some alteration to the lake in the 1880's, the course of Great Langdale Beck was controlled and the lake level was lowered making the three separate pools more distinct. The upper (western) and middle basins are around 6m deep, the lower (eastern) basin reaching 7.5m. The account of the sounding of the lake by the Brathay Exploration Group in 1979 emphasises the difficulty of getting accurate depth measurements and of defining the shores because of the depth of organic sediments on the floor and the irregular wetlands on its margins. The lake once extended from Elterwater village at its western end and down to the Skelwith Force gorge downstream. Alluvial infill is still very active from both Great Langdale and the Brathay. There are some classic areas of fen and carr vegetation, particularly around the upper and middle basins. Emergent vegetation extends into the shallow water areas for great distances.

Figure 57. a. Elter Water from the north east shore below Neaum Crag,
looking across to the Langdale Pikes in the distance.
b. Wetland on the north east shore area.
c. A glimpse of Elter Water nestling in the valley floor –
view southwards from slopes of High Close.

ESTHWAITE WATER

Gentle, mellow, pastoral are all words that come to mind when describing Esthwaite. It lies in an open valley between Windermere and Coniston Water that was excavated by a separate tongue of ice cutting a route southwards from the Langdale fells before joining with the main Windermere ice flow south of the Claife Heights. This separate tongue of ice helped with the overdeepening of the South Basin of Windermere. The valley floor is now very thickly plastered with glacial boulder clays, so much so, that rock is only seen along a minute stretch of the lake shore at its SW end. Gentle boulder clay slopes surround the lake on both sides and a series of drumlins produce some rounded peninsulas and 'near island' features at various points – notably at Strickland Ees on the west shore and at Ees Wyke near the outlet at the southern end.

Figure 60. Esthwaite looking north from the slopes above Ridding Wood (SD 358952). Strickland Ees is in the middle of the view on the western side of the lake.

The lake itself has two distinct basins. The deeper northern one has a maximum depth of 15.5m, the shallower southern one descending to just over 12m. Farmland reaches down to the lake shore over most of its length, except where wetlands cover the lowest sections. At the northern inlet end, very extensive wetlands extend up towards Hawkshead and enclose Priests Pot a small stretch of open water progressively being colonised and infilled by hydrosere development. This area and the lake basin have been studied in great detail and much is known about the vegetation and fauna. It has status as a Site of Special Scientific Interest (SSSI). Because of its lowland situation and its nutrient rich surroundings the lake is biologically very productive. A rich fauna and flora exist. The lake clearly once extended much further south than its present outlet. Alluvial infill along Cunsey Beck now encloses Out Dubs Tarn with its surrounding wetlands and marks a lower basin in the valley floor.

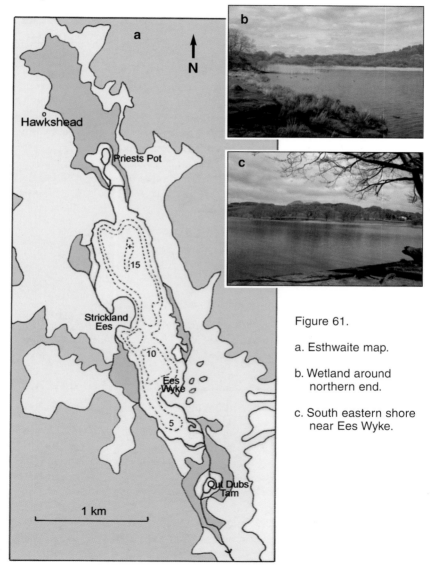

Figure 61.

a. Esthwaite map.

b. Wetland around northern end.

c. South eastern shore near Ees Wyke.

CONISTON WATER

Like Windermere, the long, slender lake of Coniston Water lies in the relatively low lying terrain of S. Lakeland. Here the landscape is subdued and contrasts markedly with the steep volcanic Coniston Fells (The Old Man of Coniston, Dow Crags and Weatherlam) which rear up suddenly around the head of the lake. It is these high fells and the high ground around the northern end of the lake that generated the ice which in its southward passage down into Morecambe Bay excavated this remarkably straight lake basin. It is notable in that it is cut completely across the geological grain of the terrain. Silurian rocks of the Windermere Supergroup (hard sandstones, mudstones and siltstones) strike SW to NE in distinct bands across the landscape, but the lake basin has been cut straight through them. None of the lake shores are particularly high. In detail they are intricate with small rocky headlands, bouldery shores, narrow belts of shingle and few pastoral shorelines. It is because the structural grain of the bedrock meets the shorelines head on, that ribs of rock and crags protrude into the lake and make for these intricate shores. This is well seen around High and Low Peel Near along the SE shore where laminated siltstones and mudstones in the Bannisdale Formation structurally control the topography.

Figure 62.
Coniston, looking south down the lake from above
Boon Crag Farm (SD 315985).

There is little alluvial infill at the lakehead as only very minor streams enter the lake here. A considerable alluvial spread has been built by Church Beck and Yewdale Beck, which have extensive catchments in the Coniston Fells and bring coarse volcanic rock debris into the lake at its NW corner. The village of Coniston stands on this alluvial infill. There is a small arcuate delta

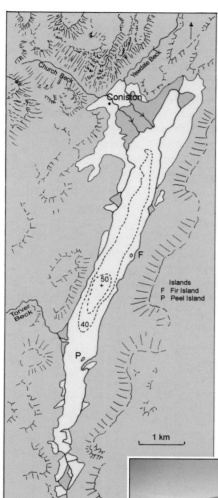

from Torver Beck midway on the west shore. Some glacial clays form part of the lower lying lake shore areas at the north east end, but elsewhere there are few low lying shore areas based on superficial deposits. The moraine complex at the southern outlet end which helps to contain the lake has already been described (Figures 12a and b).

Figure 63.

left: Coniston Water Map.

below: Northen end of the lake seen from Brantwood on eastern shore. The Old Man of Coniston (803m) and the high volcanic fells that overlook the north west corner of lake are on the skyline.

WAST WATER

Wast Water is the lake that invokes more superlatives than any other spot in the Lake District. It is Lakeland's deepest lake at 76m, with its floor 15m below sea level. Its south-eastern shore, dominated by the Screes, is an iconic view and the best example of these features anywhere in Britain. The view up the lake from its western shore to Sca Fell, Scafell Pike and the pyramid of Great Gable at its head is perhaps Lakeland's most photographed subject and the inspiration behind the logo of the Lake District National Park itself. It was a natural choice also for the front cover of this book.

Figure 64. Wast Water seen from the summit of Great Gable.
Illgill Head and the Screes on the left, steep slopes of Yewbarrow to right.

The lake basin is a textbook example of a ribbon lake – a deep, steep-sided, elongated trough with the deepest water in the middle section. The Wasdale glacier was a large, active one. Ice was generated in the highest of the central Lakeland fells and the route westwards for the ice out into the Irish Sea ice stream was direct and unobstructed. The huge lakehead delta complex has already been described. Several of the streams on its western shores produce classic small arcuate deltas of coarse angular volcanic debris (eg Nether Beck and Over Beck) (Figure 66d). Its western shores are particularly rocky, with some superb ice scoured, rounded and striated knolls of granite and volcanic rock right to the lake shore. (Figure 66). Wast Water is a rocky, primitive lake, low in nutrients with cold water and low biological productivity.

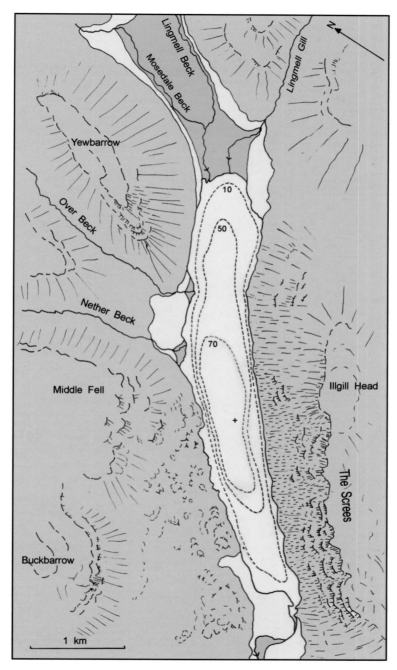

Figure 65. Wast Water

Figure 66.

a. left, the lake from Yewbarrow. The screes to the left, the low ice scoured ground on the north western shore to the right (pictures b. and c. below).

b.

c. The ice soured terrain on the north west shore – smoothed and striated exposed rock surfaces of Ennerdale Granite and surrounding volcanic rocks.

d. The small delta of coarse debris at Nether Beck on the north west shore below Yewbarrow.

ENNERDALE WATER

Ennerdale is remote by Lake District standards, with few road links on very minor roads and access to the lake and inner valley only possible on foot. Current land use management policies under the banner of 'Wild Ennerdale' are to perpetuate and enhance this vision of a wilder, natural place. The lake itself has seen a variety of attempts over past decades to modify and use the water resources for the towns of West Cumbria. It is used as a reservoir, the water level stands a little above its natural level and there is a small, low dam and retaining wall around the western end. (Figure 70a).

Figure 67. Ennerdale from High Crag

The shape of the lake is striking with its swollen, almost bulbous western outlet end. Upper Ennerdale and the upper part of the lake lie in a glacial trough, quite straight and excavated into the Ennerdale granite. The lower part of the valley and the western third of the lake is founded on Skiddaw Group rocks. Significantly many of these Skiddaw rocks have been severely metamorphosed and hardened because they were up against the igneous granite intrusion. Consequently they form very resistant crags as at Anglers' Crag on the south side of the lake and at Bowness Knott on the north side. They do account for the curious 'little isle' which stands in the middle of the lake floor (Figure 16). The ice excavating this main trough of Ennerdale was confined by the steep valley sides on the granite and in the zone of hardened Skiddaw rocks, but once clear of this confinement ice burst out from the mouth of the valley and could move away relatively easily westwards on to the West Cumbrian plain. Thick glacial boulder clay is built right across the valley mouth (Figure 11) and undoubtedly contains the lake and influences the bulbous shape of the western end. The lake has a maximum depth of 42m. Whether there is that depth of boulder clay around its outlet is

73

unknown. The upper part of the basin is distinctly trough like, with the deepest point within the confined section just above Anglers' Crag. There is a huge amount of alluvial infill at the head of the lake and a rather complex deltaic spread. Overlooking the lake head area are some complex terraces of alluvial debris and a fan of debris being brought into the valley floor by Woundell Beck. The shores are dominantly rocky. There are few bays and little wetland. Its waters are clear, biologically low in nutrients and productivity.

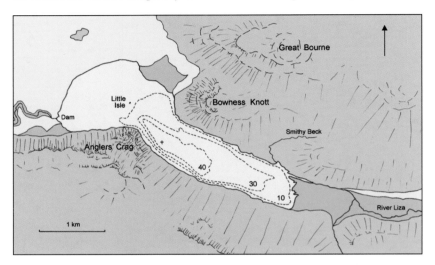

Figure 68. Ennerdale Water

Figure 69. View down the lake looking west from Long Crag (NY 155125)

Figure 70.

a.
The low dam at the outlet end, seen at a low water stage. (The lake is to the right).

b.
The small delta of pinkish granite debris built by Smithy Beck on the northern shore. (NY 123147)

c.
The lakehead delta complex of the River Liza, seen from the slopes on the north shore

LOWESWATER

Loweswater has a quiet, peaceful air and is one of the most attractive and unusual of the smaller lakes. Its configuration is slightly curious. It has a very short, almost non existent inlet stream at its head at the NW end and it is the only one of these big lakes that actually drains inwards towards the fells rather than flowing radially outwards towards the lower ground of the peripheral lowlands. This begs the question as to which way the ice was moving that created this basin. The evidence of the striations, glacial erratics and other erosional features clearly suggests it was moving NW out on to the W. Cumbrian plain, that is in the opposite direction to the present drainage. The lake is shallow (16m at its deepest point) and there is an altitudinal difference of around 48m between this low point and the col at the NE end of the valley. Whilst glacial boulder clay caps this col, it is unlikely that there is a plug of clay completely filling the valley here. All the underlying rocks are mudstones and slates of the Skiddaw Group. A relatively low col of rock could easily have been surmounted by ice. Tongues of ice from Mosedale Beck and the smaller valleys to the west (Whiteoak and High Nook) went out north westwards through Loweswater.

Figure 71. Loweswater, view from Darling Fell towards the eastern outlet end of the lake with the green fields prominent on the containing fan.

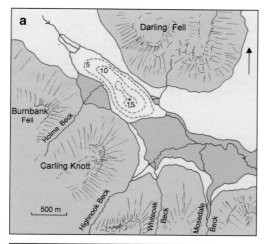

The lake is impounded by huge alluvial fans at its southern end built by High Nook and Whiteoak Becks. A superb fan from Holme Beck is now building into the lake and is the dominant geomorphological feature of the SW shore. Relatively steep slopes from Darling Fell extend down to the lake along the northern shore. Some interesting wetlands fringe the intake stream and shallow bays at the NW end and line the outlet stream at the SE end.

Figure 72.

a. Loweswater map.

b. view of the head of the lake from the slopes of Darling Fell.

c. the prominent alluvial fan at Holme Wood building out from the south shore.

CRUMMOCK WATER and BUTTERMERE

Figure 73. The two lakes seen looking up the valley from Mellbreak summit, Crummock Water in the foreground, Buttermere beyond.

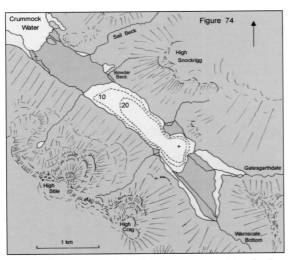

The twin lakes of Crummock Water and Buttermere have been referred to frequently in earlier sections of the book. The glacial trough in which they lie, one of the major spokes of the Lakeland wheel, has some of the finest glacial features of the district. The head of the valley with its two distinct branches of Warnscale Bottom and Gatesgarthdale were conduits for ice generated in the heart of the Lakeland fells. Both are steep sided glaciated troughs cut into volcanic rocks. Down valley, however, strong geological contrasts appear on either side. Skiddaw Group mudstones, sandstones and slates form the north west side, whereas opposite, a complex mixture of resistant volcanics and the Ennerdale granite produces the steep terrain along the SW side of Buttermere and the western shores of Crummock Water. Many of the shoreline details illustrate differences in the bedrock geology.

Buttermere is a lake that is comparatively deep for its size, with few areas of shallow water. Nearly two thirds of the lake has depths of more than 15m. The basin is a steep sided trough with a remarkably flat floor. At the lake head there is an extensive alluvial infill. The classic arcuate deltas built out into the lake by Comb Beck and Hassnesshow Beck have already been described in detail (Figure 33). Similarly the isthmus area separating Buttermere from Crummock Water at its northern end has been illustrated in Figure 35 and accompanying text.

Figure 75.

The head of Buttermere. The valley of Gatesgarthdale is to the left, the ridge of Fleetwith Pike runs down towards the lakehead and Warnscale Bottom is the valley at the extreme right.

Figure 76.

The steep volcanic slopes on the south west side of Buttermere. The cirque of Burtness Comb is in the centre of the view.

Crummock Water is serene. Although it is used as a reservoir for the towns of W. Cumbria and the present lake level is maintained just a metre or so above its natural height by a low concrete wall and dam at its lower end (Figure 79a), it retains a natural feel. The western shore is dominated by the steep slopes of Mellbreak, formed of toughened Skiddaw Group rocks. Similar rocks form the even steeper fell slopes of Whiteless Pike, Grassmoor and Whiteside, which, although set back slightly from the lake, tower over its eastern shores. Whilst glacial erosion has excavated the lake basin and steepened and scoured the fellsides and valley floor, more recent slope processes account for the detailed topography of the lower valley slopes and many stretches of the lake shores. The steep fellsides formed of hard, silty rocks of the Skiddaw Group have proved highly susceptible to rock slope failure, instability and break up, and have been riven by gully erosion and slope wash. Debris has accumulated as aprons of talus on the lower slopes and has been washed by streams on to the lake margins. Fans of debris have been built out towards the lake on the west by Scale Beck and by small rivulets that move material down the flanks of Mellbreak. On the east side a fan of debris fills in the enclave of Rannerdale. Further north below Grassmoor End, huge accumulations cover the low ground around Lanthwaite Green and extend right to the lake edge where they can be seen in low cliffs. (NY 155205).

Figure 77. Crummock Water from Rannerdale Knotts looking across to Mellbreak

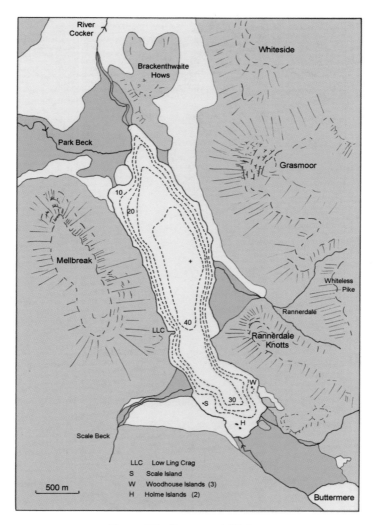

Figure 78. Crummock Water.

The lake itself has a simple, elongated form, with little shallow water and very few bays. Along both the west and east shores the basin drops steeply down to the relatively flat floor, which lies at an average of around 40m. The deepest point of 43.9m is close to the central point. A large drumlin and banks of glacial clays plug the north west end of the basin around Highpark. (Figure 26). The drumlin has been cliffed along its lake edge and it partly encloses the fine beach described in an earlier section (Figure 37). These glacial materials at the northern end clearly partly contain the lake. However it is alluvial debris from Park Beck, emanating from Loweswater, and entering the lake near its northern tip, that really plugs the outlet area of the basin. It pushes the outlet stream up to the foot of the prominent solid rocky knoll of Brackenthwaite Hows that stands proud in the valley floor here. The River Cocker encounters bedrock shortly downstream from the exit, confirming the lake lies in a rock basin.

Figure 79.
Crummock Water.

a. retaining wall and small pump house building at northern end.

b. Grassmoor End towering over the northern end of the lake.

c. The deltaic infill at the mouth of Rannerdale. View from Rannerdale Knotts.

d. Woodhouse Islands at southern end of Crummock Water.
Mellbreak in the distance.

DERWENT WATER

In the heyday of Victorian times, with visitors coming to the Lake District in great numbers, Derwent Water acquired the accolade of "The Queen of the Lakes". It deserves that title because it stands out amongst the big lakes as being different. Its broad oval shape and the immense variety of landscapes and vistas within such a small area around its shores, make it unique. Its intricate shoreline of bays and promontories, crags, beaches, woods and wetlands; and its numerous islands create a scene that matches, and arguably surpasses, any other part of Lakeland.

Figure 80. Derwent Water from Latrigg. View is looking south, Keswick in the foreground

The lake is shallow for its size, at the deepest point being only 22m. The floor of the basin is very irregular. Four large drumlin islands dominate the northern half and numerous small rocky islets and shoals of rocky outcrops protrude above the water at various points.

The whole of the lake basin has been excavated by ice into Skiddaw Group rocks. The important north-south Derwent Water Fault is aligned precisely along the eastern shore and brings volcanic rocks to form the shore area and the imposing line of steep crags and slopes that face the basin on that side (Walla Crag, Falcon Crag, Brown Knotts, Ashness Fell and Shepherds Crag). The width and configuration of the basin is partly due to the relative weakness of the Skiddaw Group rocks; material that the ice found easy to break down and carry away. It is also due in part to the particularly tough volcanic rocks in the area of the Jaws of Borrowdale, upstream of the head of the lake. Here, northward moving ice found it hard to erode. There was a bottleneck effect. Ice was squeezed hard as it passed through the constriction

83

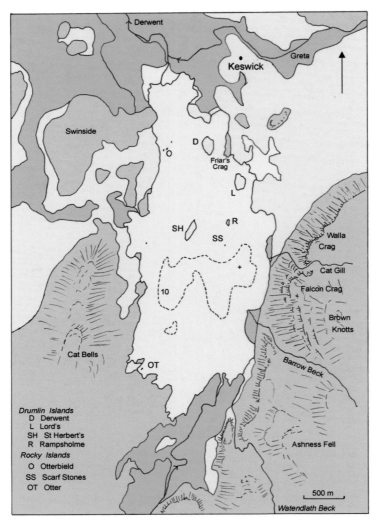

Figure 81. Derwent Water

of the Jaws, probably moving relatively quickly through the narrow part. All of the Jaws area however, was completely overridden by ice and heavily scoured. The catchment of Borrowdale and its tributaries was a large one, making it one of the most powerful glacier systems within the district. The Jaws thus formed a major step in the long profile of the Borrowdale glacier. Once ice had passed over and through this, it flowed down under compressive flow into the more benign ground of the Skiddaw rocks. Ice from the side tributary valley of Watendlath Beck supplemented the flow into the lake basin and helped in the erosion.

Figure 82. Derwent Water, view looking north from Grange Crags.

The lake is contained at its northern end by glacial debris and extensive spreads of alluvium, most of it brought into the valley by the River Greta from the east. This stream has a large catchment and hence carries a large sediment load. The alluvial debris has filled in the valley floor between the array of drumlins and mounds of glacial clays in the eastern side of the valley north of Keswick. The thickness of the alluvial spread forming the low lying isthmus of land that separates the lake from Bassenthwaite Lake, is not known in any detail. Recent data from the Environment Agency suggest it is no more than 20m thick. Low knolls of Skiddaw Group rocks protrude through the alluvial cover, particularly close to Portinscale on the western side, suggesting a rock bar across the trough floor. Clearly Derwent Water and Bassenthwaite Lake were at one time joined as a continuous sheet of water. At times of severe flooding today (as in the severe storms of November 2009) water extended right across this isthmus uniting the two lakes. The difference in height between the two lakes is in the order of only 6m.

The water level in Derwent Water changes quite rapidly, rising and falling as much as 3m between times of high and low rainfall. The townsfolk of Keswick have for many years erected plaques on the promontory of Friar's Crag recording particularly low and high levels of the lake. This oscillation is not just a reflection of varying rainfall patterns, which Lakeland and Borrowdale in particular, with its high rainfall regime, are very prone to, but is also partly due to erosion of the natural sill of glacial clay along the short section of the River Derwent between the two lakes. Artificial schemes to maintain the sill are in place. A consequence of these constant changes in the level of Derwent Water is that many of the beaches are wide and in periods of storms sizeable waves generated by strong winds usually blowing down the lake, move beach material extensively and scour the shoreline areas (seen particularly in Calfclose Bay, Figure 84b).

Figure 83. a. Derwent Water from Catbells. The steep slopes of Walla Crags, formed of volcanic rocks lie on the far side of the lake.

Figure 83. b. The northern end of Derwent Water seen from Catbells. The drumlin islands are prominent in the view

Figure 84.

a. above.
The promontory
of Friar's Crag –
a dyke like
intrusion of
resistant diorite.

b. left
Broad stony
beach in
Calfclose Bay.
Snow capped
Skiddaw beyond.

There is extensive alluvial infill at the head of the lake, a process that is still active. The classic bird's foot delta of the River Derwent has already been described. (Figure 31). The arcuate delta built into the lake by Barrow Beck was also explained in an earlier section. A similar but slightly smaller arcuate delta from Cat Gill is also seen on the eastern shore.

Important wetland areas infill several of the bays – notably at the Ings on the north east shore, areas near the outlet at Portinscale, at Town Cass near Keswick and in several small bays on the west shore.

BASSENTHWAITE LAKE

Morphologically Bassenthwaite Lake is really a simple, straight-forward feature. It has a relatively simple outline and a distinctly 'ribbon lake' shape with a single deep area close to its centre. Importantly it has extensive areas of shallow water, both at its northern and southern ends. This has impacted particularly on its importance for wildlife and vegetation around the shores. Considerable infill at the southern end reflects the huge sediment loads being brought into the valley floor by the Greta, the Derwent from Derwent Water and the Newlands Beck system from the fells to the south west. Low alluvial land, wetlands and a complex delta at the mouth of the Derwent dominate the southern end. Glacial clays extend across the low lying ground at its northern end and partly contain the lake. It is likely that the Derwent may have exited via the Dubwath valley at some early stage of the deglaciation phase, rather than via its present outlet at the north west corner at Ouse Bridge.

Figure 85. The head of Bassenthwaite Lake from Latrigg.

All the lake lies on Skiddaw Group rocks but rock is not a prominent feature of the lake shores. Only on the northern part of the west shore do rocky slopes approach anywhere near the lake. Elsewhere, the steep slopes are set well back from the lake. Gentle ground, covered with glacial clays stretches along the eastern shore which is indented with shallow bays and headlands. In fact gentle boulder clay shores are a particular feature of Bassenthwaite – green pastures existing right to the lake edge where erosion has isolated the very large erratic boulders from the boulder clay, leaving them stranded by the waters edge. Many of these stand out as 'erratics' as they are mainly volcanic rocks brought down valley by the ice from the Borrowdale or Thirlmere valleys high in the catchment. Similar shores exist close to Blackstock Point (NY 223273) on the west shore (Figure 88). An intrusion of a resistant igneous diorite forms the small rounded promontory covered by Bowness Wood on the east shore (NY 221290) (Figure 86 and 89).

Figure 86.

a.

The complex delta area at the lake head. The River Derwent enters from the left. View from the slopes of Dodd.

b.

Boulder clay shoreline at Broadness. A gentle, grassy shore area scattered with large volcanic erratic boulders. Typical of many Bassenthwaite Lake shores.

c.

Wetland (foreground) in Bowness Bay. Beyond, the wooded low hill covered with Bowness Wood – an intrusion of diorite.

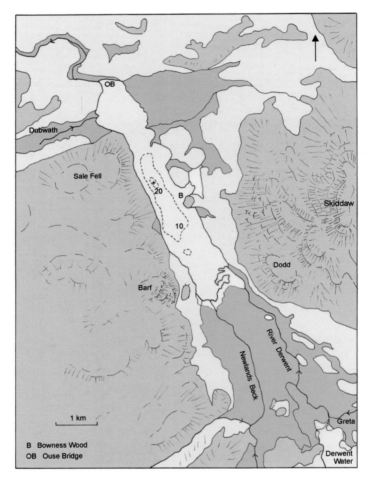

Figure 87. Basenthwaite Lake

Figure 88.

The western lake shore just south of Blackstock Point (NY223275). The shallow nature of the lake is revealed at low water stages (as in this picture) when extensive gravelly stretches emerge. The long spit feature where the people are standing is normally under water.

90

Figure 89. The lake from the slopes of Ullock Pike.

The lake has the status of a National Nature Reserve and a Site of Special Scientific Interest (SSSI) because of both its fauna and lake shore flora. It is a quiet and relatively inaccessible lake in spite of the fact that the busy A66 trunk road follows part of its western shore. There are few public access points, the wetlands at its southern end are impassable and much of the eastern and northern shores are in private ownership. Recreational activities on the lake are severely restricted. The lake has significant ecological problems, threats of pollution, too much silt entering the basin affecting the spawning of fish and invasive fish and plant species putting the native fauna and flora at risk. Fell erosion, river bank erosion, field drainage and mine waste are the main causes of increased sedimentation into the lake over recent decades. Pollution from the urban population and significant changes in land use have all triggered problems.

THIRLMERE

Thirlmere has been so altered from its original state by its damming in 1894 to provide a water supply for the City of Manchester that much of its interest as a landscape feature has been lost. A huge masonry dam 260 m long was constructed across its northern outlet, the lake level raised 16.46 m and hence we now have artificial shorelines, restricted access and much of the valley obscured with forestry plantations.

Figure 90. Thirlmere, looking north from above Middlesteads Gill.

The north-south alignment of the Thirlmere valley follows the Coniston Fault that slices through the volcanic rocks of the central part of the district. This structure accounts for the extremely straight valley and the alignment of the very low col of Dunmail Raise at its head. The fault also determines the line of St. John's in the Vale, the route the outlet stream takes from the lake. Thirlmere has quite a small catchment, but the ice that cut this trough was being generated right in the heart of the Lakeland ice dome and was clearly sufficient to create the glacial trough and significantly deepen its floor. Both sides are steep with distinct shoulders to the trough, indicating substantial deepening in the last glacial phase. The lake appears confined, but this may be the illusion created by reservoir construction and the fact that for the most part the view of the lake now is from above on the fellside slopes. At the northern end the ice was able to override a series of major rocky ridges and knolls in the valley floor. Ice, less confined by the trough walls, moved NW down the Naddle route to join the Borrowdale ice stream over the Keswick area and out by the Bassenthwaite valley, but it also moved NE via St. John's in the Vale to flow out towards the Eden Valley.

Originally two separate ribbon lakes lay in this valley. They were linked by a short, narrow channel, which, before the reservoir was constructed, was bridged. The upper lake lay in a somewhat irregular basin with its deepest point of nearly 30m near its head. The far smaller lower lake was only slightly shallower, but was a quite separate rock basin in the valley floor. The area between the two lakes was partly a deltaic spread built into the valley floor by Thrang Gill and Middlesteads Gill coming in on the western side of the trough. The trough floor and the lower flanks of the valley were irregular with a series of rocky ridges and ice-scoured knolls coming down to the lake on the western shores. Some of these can still be seen as the islands in the reservoir (Deergarth and Hawes How) and in the many rocky lumps that are revealed at times when the water level is drawn down.

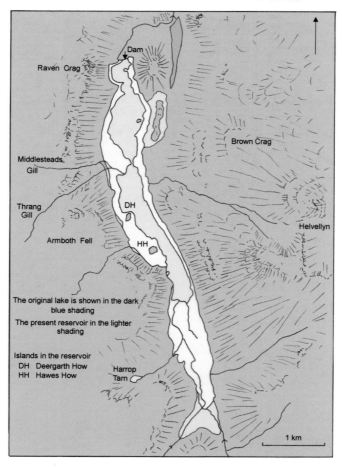

Figure 91. Thirlmere.

Figure 92
a. right

The original valley with its two lake basins. View looking north. The delta from Middle-steads and Thrang Gills is clearly seen on the left. The narrow neck of land between the two basins has a bridge.

b. left

The dam (centre of view). The lake is standing at a relatively low level – the harsh, bare shorelines stand out when the drawdown on the reservoir is at this extreme stage.

c. The northern end of the lake from Brown Crag (NY328176) on the eastern side.

ULLSWATER

Ullswater, the second largest of these big lakes, is a complex feature, notable for its distinctive dog-leg, inverse S shape. Its three distinct reaches are three separate deep basins. The short upper basin drops to a depth of around 47 m. The long middle reach is the deepest at 62.5 m, and the lower reach the shallowest at around 39 m. At water level at most points, it is possible to see only a relatively small part of this large lake. The upper and middle reaches have a 'mountain' character with steep fellsides coming close to the shores (Figure 95). The lower reach is more open with gentle slopes and pastures falling to the water's edge. As you approach the outlet end at Pooley Bridge there is a feeling you are leaving the Lake District and emerging into a new landscape.

The reasons for this complex shape lie with the complexities of the underlying geology. The lake cuts across three distinctive rock types (Figure 93). Skiddaw Group slates, shales and mudstones underlie much of the middle and lower reaches and tend to form low ground. Resistant volcanic lavas and tuffs of the Borrowdale Volcanic Group on the other hand make the upstanding and rugged fells around the upper basin and the steep fells of the southern shores. At the extreme northern end the very different Mell Fell Conglomerates reach to the shores and form the outlet area near Pooley Bridge. More important are the structures within these rocks. A major SW-NE broad upfold (more or less along the line of the lake) has brought the Skiddaw rocks to the surface, but the erosive power of the ice was able to slice through this arched structure and break its crest. The fold is made more complex by a network of strong faults which chop this area into pieces and form weak lines which erosion can exploit. The faults have not only moved vertically but also horizontally, sliding blocks of rock against each other and lifting them up and down into a mosaic of different shaped interlocking pieces. The position of the Howtown Fault explains the kink in the lake between the middle and lower reaches. Faults delineate the alignment of the upper reach and the bend in the lake between the upper and middle sections. The Skiddaw rocks provide the lower, more open shores of the lower reach with the Mell Fell Conglomerates at the extreme northern end near Pooley Bridge, standing out as prominent, rounded hills (Figure 97).

With this geological complexity it is not surprising that we have a huge variety of shorelines. Volcanic rocks form the steep, craggy shores of Hallin Fell, Place Fell and the Stybarrow Crag stretches of the upper reach. Volcanic rocks also reach the northern shore area around Gowbarrow Park. Boulder clays lie over much of the lower ground of the Skiddaw Group rocks along the northern shores of the middle reach (Glencoyne Park and Swinburn's

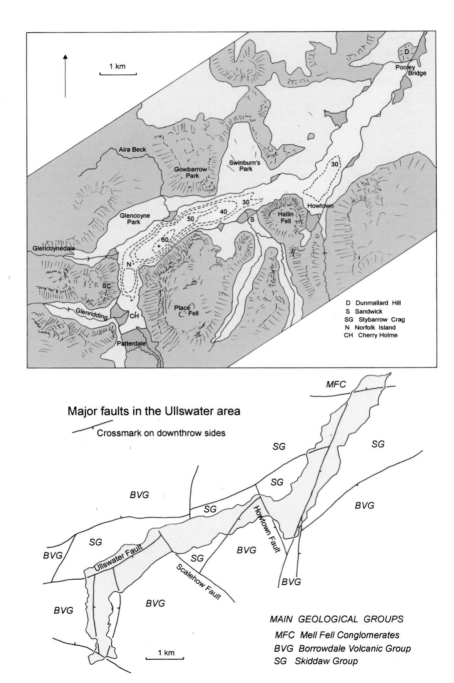

Figure 93. Ullswater, map above, geological interpretation below.

Park) and along the SE shore from Pooley Bridge. These form gentle ground with parkland and pastures extending right to the shores. Many of these boulder clay areas have been shaped into rounded headlands (Nebs) and smooth bays.

Figure 94. The middle reach of Ullswater from Glencoyne. Place Fell to the right, delta of Glencoyne Beck in the foreground. View down the lake.

Figure 95. The upper reach of Ullswater from Gowbarrow.

At the very head of the lake there is an extensive stretch of alluvial infill at Patterdale, much of it edged with wetland vegetation. Ullswater also has some classic arcuate deltas. The largest is at Glenridding where sedimentation has been accelerated by the movement of mine waste from the Greenside lead mining installations up valley. Glencoyndale Beck, Aira Beck and Sandwick Beck are other good examples (Figure 96).

Figure 96. Deltas: Left, Aira Beck, right, Glenridding

Figure 97. The rounded Dumallard Hill at Pooley Bridge.
Formed of Devonian age resistant conglomerates.

The outlet end of Ullswater is difficult to evaluate. The Mell Fell Conglomerates come right to the shore on the western side of the outlet stream, with the steep wooded slopes of Dunmallard Hill overlooking the bridging point at Pooley Bridge. On the eastern side, the much lower shore area is in boulder clay, but there is no obvious topographical terminal moraine feature. Down valley from the outlet area there are extensive spreads of glacial sands and gravels, flushed out of the valley from the wasting ice, but the extent to which they plug the valley is unclear, as we have no evidence of the height of the bedrock below.

Figure 98. Distant view of Brothers Water from the head of the Kirkstone Pass – looking north.

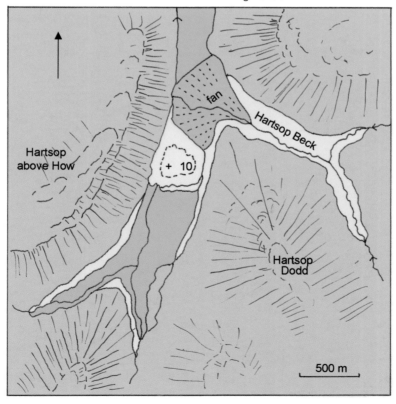

Now practically the smallest of these 17 big lakes, Brothers Water was undoubtedly at one time considerably larger. It has a high sediment input from its extensive catchment area. The present spread of alluvial infill at the lake head extends up valley for around 900 m, about twice the length of the present lake. It is a classic example of a small lake contained by an alluvial fan. The fan built by Hartsop Beck extends right across the floor of the glacial trough, the distinct triangular shape of the northern shore being defined by the southern edge of the fan. The lake is 16.7 m deep near its centre. 6 metre coring of the sediments on its floor did not reach bedrock, so there is a considerable depth of accumulated debris in the basin. The lake level stands at 158 m. The fan has an extremely gentle slope and stands only a metre or so above lake level. Downstream in the Patterdale area bedrock exists in the valley floor at 150 m which seems to confirm that Brothers Water occupies a rock basin and that the alluvial fan is merely enhancing the water level by a few metres.

A very steep, rectilinear rocky slope with a thin covering of scree debris from the Hartsop above How ridge descends right down to the western shore. A SSW-NNE fault in the underlying volcanic bedrock explains the straight alignment of this shore. On the east the almost equally steep slopes of Hartsop Dodd defines this side of the glacial trough. All the area is in the resistant Borrowdale Volcanic Group rocks (mainly dacites and ignimbrites here). Wetlands and carr woodlands fringe the southern shores of the lake. The present inlet stream has been controlled and canalised to secure the low lying pasture land and does not follow its original line, which probably lay to the west. Typical of many lakehead inlet streams its mouth is bifurcated and gravel is constantly being built out into the shallow lake waters.

Figure 100. The Southeast corner of Brothers Water. View looking south across the wetland fringing the lake towards Dovedale and Dove Crag.

HAWES WATER

Like Thirlmere the original Hawes Water has been destroyed by damming to create a water supply reservoir. Also like Thirlmere, originally there were two small ribbon lakes separated by a deltaic spread, here from Measand Beck on the northern shore. The original lake was raised 29 m by the construction of the dam, which was completed in 1941. The original upper basin was a simple elongated trough that reached a depth of 28 m close to its centre. The shorter, much shallower northern most part of the lake, below the Measand delta, reached only 14 m in depth.

Hawes Water is an open, steep sided, gently curving glaciated trough cut deep into the volcanic bedrock and some complex intrusive rocks at its lower end. The new lake now extends a considerable way up valley. Boulder clay lies along many of the present lake shores, particularly on the NW shore and in the tributary valley of Riggindale.

Figure 101. Haweswater –
looking down the lake from Heron Crag.

101

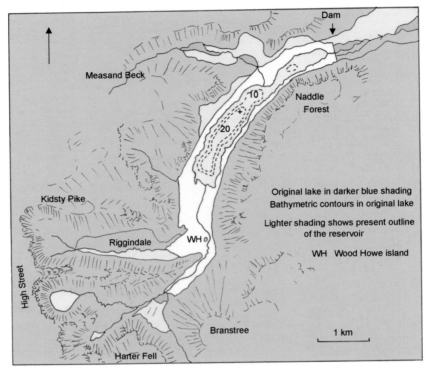

Figure 102. Haweswater.

Figure 103. At times of drawdown a wide, bare, shore zone is exposed.
The reservoir seen from Harter Fell.

Figure 104.

a. right: The Haweswater Dam – a hollow, massive-buttress concrete structure, completed in 1941. Seen from the southern end.

b. below right and c. at foot of page: The Haweswater reservoir at the end of July 1984. After a prolonged period of drought in the spring and early summer of 1984, by the end of July the level of the reservoir had dropped by over 11 metres. Whilst it was not down to the level of the two original lakes, it was at an all time low. The upper arm of the reservoir was completely dry (picture b). Much of the lower part of Riggindale was also dry and Wood Howe was no longer an island (extreme right of picture c) More dramatic

were the remains of the old settlement of Mardale which were revealed once again 40 years after they had been abandoned and drowned by the construction of the reservoir. The old Chapel Bridge over the beck (still intact) is well seen in the centre of the picture c. below, also the stone walls of the old fields and lanes around the hamlet.

THE AUTHOR

Dr. Alan Smith is now retired from an academic career. He has written several books, papers and guides on Lakeland geology and geomorphology. He is a Past President and General Secretary of the Cumberland Geological Society. He lives in Keswick.

All the maps and diagrams have been compiled and drawn especially for this book by the author.

All the photographs are also by the author.

Figures 2 and 3 are taken from "Bathymetrical Survey of the English Lakes" by Hugh Robert Mill, published in *The Geographical Journal, vol. 6, 1895.*

Figure 92a, a photograph of the original Thirlmere is in the Keswick Museum and Art Gallery. Copyright has expired.

COVER PHOTOGRAPHS

Front cover: Wast Water – looking up to the head of the lake from the west shore near Countess Beck. The pyramid of Great Gable is in the centre of the view in the distance. To the left is Yewbarrow and to the right are the slopes of Lingmell and the northern end of The Screes.

Back cover:
Upper: Haweswater. The head of the lake from the roadside near Rowan-treethwaite Beck, with the wooded promontory of The Rigg in the centre view.
Lower: Buttermere from Rannerdale Knotts.